The Open U

T357
Structural integrity:
designing against failure

BLOCK 1
STRESS ANALYSIS

PART 1: STRESS
PART 2: STRAIN

This publication forms part of an Open University course T357 *Structural integrity: designing against failure*. Details of this and other Open University courses can be obtained from the Student Registration and Enquiry Service, The Open University, PO Box 197, Milton Keynes MK7 6BJ, United Kingdom: tel. +44 (0)845 300 60 90, email general-enquiries@open.ac.uk

Alternatively, you may visit the Open University website at http://www.open.ac.uk where you can learn more about the wide range of courses and packs offered at all levels by The Open University.

To purchase a selection of Open University course materials visit http://www.ouw.co.uk, or contact Open University Worldwide, Walton Hall, Milton Keynes MK7 6AA, United Kingdom for a brochure. tel. +44 (0)1908 858793; fax +44 (0)1908 858787; email ouw-customer-services@open.ac.uk

The Open University
Walton Hall, Milton Keynes
MK7 6AA

First published 2007. Second edition 2009.

Edited and designed by The Open University.

Typeset by SR Nova Pvt. Ltd, Bangalore, India.

Printed in the United Kingdom by Latimer Trend and Company Ltd, Plymouth.

ISBN 978 0 7492 5266 3

2.1

FSC
Mixed Sources
Product group from well-managed forests and other controlled sources
Cert no. SGS-COC-005493
www.fsc.org
© 1996 Forest Stewardship Council

The paper used in this publication contains pulp sourced from forests independently certified to the Forest Stewardship Council (FSC) principles and criteria. Chain of custody certification allows the pulp from these forests to be tracked to the end use (see www.fsc.org).

CONTENTS

INTRODUCTION TO STRUCTURAL INTEGRITY   **3**

PART 1 STRESS   **13**

  1   The concept of stress   17

  2   Normal stress   22

  3   Shear stress   31

  4   Stresses in arbitrary directions   40

  5   Describing stress in two dimensions   49

  6   Principal stresses   62

  7   Mohr's circle   67

  8   The stress tensor: describing stress in three dimensions   78

  9   Summary   83

  Learning outcomes   84

  Answers to exercises   85

  Answers to self-assessment questions   93

  Acknowledgements   99

PART 2 STRAIN   **101**

  1   The concept of strain   105

  2   Normal strain   106

  3   Shear strain   112

  4   Plane strain   116

  5   Relating strain to stress   119

  6   Strain measurement: experimental stress analysis   130

  7   Freight container case study   149

  8   Summary   158

  Learning outcomes   159

  Answers to exercises   160

  Answers to self-assessment questions   164

  Acknowledgements   173

INTRODUCTION TO STRUCTURAL INTEGRITY

This course is about the concepts and theories that underpin the field of engineering known as *Structural integrity* – that is, the safe design and assessment of load-bearing structures in their entirety, including any individual components from which they may have been constructed. Aspects of structural integrity are implemented in almost every engineering design process, even if the engineer or designer does not necessarily think of it in that way. In this course, we have separated the skills and knowledge associated with expertise in structural integrity under two headings: *Stress analysis*, which is the study of how applied forces lead to internal stresses in structures; and *Fracture mechanics*, which is the study of components and structures containing cracks.

EXERCISE 1

(a) Identify four components or structures that experience loads during their operation.

(b) Can you identify components or structures that do not experience significant loads during operation?

In thinking about part (b) you should have come to the conclusion that virtually nothing is entirely load free. At the very least, any component or structure has to bear its own weight, irrespective of any external loads. A designer might make an intuitive judgment that the loads on a product do not need to be considered, but hopefully that would be underpinned by an educated estimate of what the forces are likely to be and what intensity of load, or stress, the assembly can support. And this is why the concept of stress is important: the limiting material property we are dealing with is 'strength', and for safe operation the stresses experienced during use need to be well below the material strength.

Engineering failures can be spectacular and highly publicized, especially when they result in death and destruction; but the failure of a household product can be more immediately annoying, and just as indicative of a poor design.

EXERCISE 2

Make a list of three structural integrity failures of which you have experience. In other words, list three single items, assemblies or structures that have snapped, collapsed, fractured or just plain fallen to pieces in your home, car or workplace, for example. Try to make them as different as possible – so don't choose three smashed pieces of china. Try to think *why* these items might have failed, paying particular attention to how they were loaded during use and whether this loading was different when failure occurred.

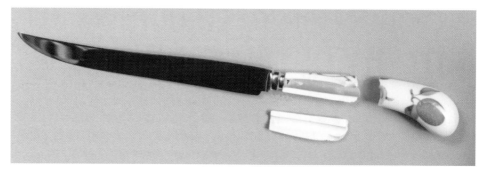

Figure 1   Poorly designed broken cake-knife handle

We have all experienced component failures in one form or another. In many cases this is because something has reached the end of its working life due to a slow-acting failure mechanism: car tyres wear slowly and will eventually burst if not replaced; the filament in a light bulb slowly loses material until it cannot sustain the applied voltage and melts. Failures where something has been so badly designed that it cannot withstand its intended loading during normal use are rarer, but they do occur nonetheless. Take a look at Figure 1, which shows the broken handle of a decorative cake knife, the sort that gets used only on 'special' occasions. In fact, this example of failure was caused by poor design. Note that a metal 'tang' extends from the blade into the handle as a means of reinforcement. In this case the tang was simply too short to strengthen the ceramic handle sufficiently against the bending loads that arose during cutting. The failure occurred while the knife was being used at a wedding reception and resulted in blood-soaked icing.

In this course we will use the shorthand 'Pa' or 'pascal' for the units of stress and pressure, $N\ m^{-2}$ (newtons per square metre).

The elbow connector shown in Figure 2 is another case of poor design having disastrous consequences. The elbow was part of pressurized pipework used in a hydraulically powered waste compactor that ruptured during use, causing severe injury to the operator. Subsequent analysis indicated that the wall thickness and material properties of the connector were just not adequate for the job of containing pressures over 17 MPa ($17 \times 10^6\ N\ m^{-2}$). You may have had similar experiences of structural failure, although hopefully more mundane.

Figure 2   Ruptured elbow connector; the combination of thin walls and weak material could not stand the internal pressure

The way the load intensity, or stress, varies within a material is also important. If we can understand and quantify the internal stress distribution then we are some way towards figuring out why the failure occurred. But not only that: we can also redesign structures so that they are less likely to fail next time round. Or better still, we can avoid it ever happening in the first place. In other words, stress analysis is a very useful tool. Often the calculation of stress is relatively straightforward, but for complicated components and systems of components, with multiple loads and varying material properties, more complex analyses are required. This course will give you the understanding and skills required to undertake and interpret such analyses.

It is often not possible to design something to withstand any foreseeable load. The laptop on which I am writing this is reasonably robust, but I would not expect it to keep working properly after I had reversed my car over it. Figure 3 shows a couple of examples of 'overload' failures that occurred because the structures were subjected to a loading for which they were not designed. A bicycle wheel is perfectly capable of carrying the load of two or three merry students provided that the loading direction is approximately in the plane of the wheel itself, where it is strongest. But a sideways impact can easily cause buckling (Figure 3a). Similarly, a stepladder leg is designed to bear heavy vertical loads, but a significant lateral force will cause it to bend (Figure 3b). More extreme, earthquake-induced, overload failures are shown in Figures 4 and 5. Of course, it is extremely difficult to design a building that will withstand any magnitude of earthquake, but there are design philosophies that can

Figure 3 (a) Bent bicycle wheel and (b) stepladder leg: the result of loading in unexpected directions

(a)   (b)

Even a single column collapse in a multi-storey building places greater load on underlying storeys, which then collapse in turn leading to multiple floors stacked upon each other, like pancakes. This is due primarily to the use of low-cost structural columns of inadequate strength.

Figure 4   Failed reinforced-concrete column, Kobe earthquake, Japan, 1995

Figure 5   'Pancaking', common in the aftermath of the 1999 Izmit earthquake in Turkey

make them more 'resistant', including methods of damping vibrations and trying to ensure that damage, when it does occur, does not lead to total collapse of the structure. Nevertheless, under such circumstances engineers and designers are often faced with decisions about balancing effective design against cost and the likelihood of catastrophic failure.

I indicated earlier that many failures occur after a product has been in service for some time: such as the wear of a car tyre, or corrosion of the car body itself. It is also possible for components to fail because of a combination of a manufacturing defect with the applied loading or with the environmental conditions during use. Figure 6 illustrates the link from mechanisms such as corrosion, fatigue (repeated loading) and creep (continuous deformation under load) to failure in some form.

So in addition to knowing the stresses in a material arising from the applied loading, depending on the environment in which the component is used it may be necessary to consider the effects of corrosion, wear, creep and fatigue. The effects of any of these

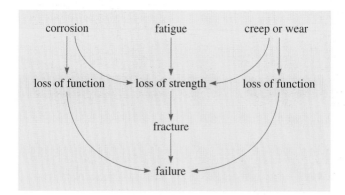

Figure 6   Routes to failure from different mechanisms

Figure 7 Sad, old and rusty: the West Pier, Brighton

mechanisms can weaken a structure to the point where it can no longer bear the loads for which it was originally designed, as shown in Figure 7.

The study of structures that contain cracks from the day they are made is sufficiently important for us to dedicate a large proportion of this course to it. Fracture mechanics allows us to assess whether cracks will be safe under the applied loads. But even in cases where we can be reasonably sure that there are no cracks of any significant size, there is still the possibility that fatigue loading or another mechanism can cause them to initiate and grow, as illustrated in Figures 8 and 9.

There are also complex resonant loading cases that can cause failure. You may well remember the publicity surrounding the 'wobbling' of the Millennium footbridge in London when it was opened. More spectacular was the actual collapse of the Tacoma

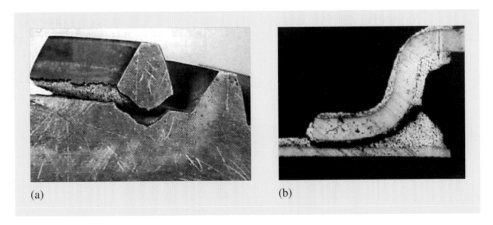

(a)   (b)

Figure 8 (a) Gear failure – tooth breakage from a fatigue crack that started at the root and arising from bending loads due to the contact driving torque; (b) fatigue failure in a solder joint due to expansion and contraction stresses caused by thermal cycling

Figure 9   Steel pressure vessel, 1.7 m in diameter and 15 cm thick, that failed during a hydraulic proof test at 3.4 MPa. The crack that caused the accident grew from a small (5 mm) embedded welding crack

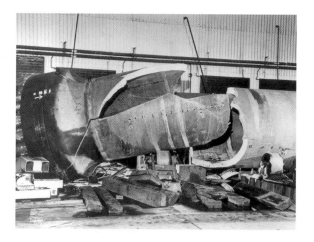

Narrows suspension bridge in America in 1940 (see Figure 10). The structure was perceived in its time as the pinnacle of structural lightness, grace and flexibility in bridge design. However, it met its end within four months of construction because of a woeful inability to cope with resonance effects in moderate winds – only 45 mph on the day of collapse.

At first, we will be concerned with static loading, rather than with dynamic effects. Later we will cover fatigue loading, but we will not cover more complex vibrational modes and effects in this course.

DVD

The Tacoma Narrows failure is covered briefly in 'The riddle of the Tay Bridge disaster' programme on the course DVD.

Figure 10   Tacoma Narrows bridge: going … going … gone

All the examples I have used here are of things that have failed, which is perhaps not the best illustration of the design process. However, learning from failures can give insight into why the failure occurred and how to avoid it in the future. Successful designs that simply do the job rarely make the headlines.

ACTIVITY 1

Have another look at that list of failures you made for Exercise 2. Are you any the wiser as to the origin of the failure, in terms of the loading on the component when it failed?

Keep that list tucked away safely, I'm going to ask you to have a look at it again later. In the meantime, the course now starts from scratch, with a formal look at what stresses and strains are, and how we work with them in analysing designs.

ANSWERS TO EXERCISES

EXERCISE 1

(a) A few that spring to mind are: the wing of an aeroplane; the wheel of a car; the keyboard of a computer; the control wheel of an iPod; the leg of a chair; a door handle; a bookcase … I'm sure you get the idea.

(b) This is a bit trickier, and perhaps the question is a little unfair, but I hope that thinking about this will have shown you just how universal the presence of loading is. Something like the casing of a television set may not be highly loaded during use, but will be loaded when the set is carried, for instance; it also has to bear its own weight without deformation. In fact I can't think of any components that won't experience loads at some point during their lifetime, even if they are only handling loads.

EXERCISE 2

You have obviously made a personal list and I can't really help you with that, but the process is useful because it has allowed you to begin to engage with how to assess structural failure.

You may be feeling pleased with yourself, or you may be thinking how little you know. In any case, I would like you to keep your list safe, along with your interpretation of each failure.

ACKNOWLEDGEMENTS

Grateful acknowledgement is made to the following sources:

FIGURES

Figure 2: Reprinted from *Engineering Failure Analysis*, Vol. 10, No. 2, Mirshams, R.A. and Sabbaghian, M. 'Failure Analysis of an Elbow Tube Fitting', pp. 215–221. Copyright 2003, with permission from Elsevier.

Figure 3(a): © Simo Bogdanovic/Alamy.

Figure 4: © Kawase Shinichi/Digitalization: Kobe University Library.

Figure 7: © Paul Carstairs/Alamy.

Figure 8(a): From www.tribology.co.uk/services/investigate/g01-0.html

Figure 8(b): From www.calce.umd.edu/general/newsletter/news/9-1993.html

Figure 9: © TWI Ltd.

Figure 10: Courtesy of University of Washington Libraries, Special Collections [UW20731; UW21422; UW21413].

PART 1
STRESS

CONTENTS

1	**THE CONCEPT OF STRESS**	**17**
2	**NORMAL STRESS**	**22**
3	**SHEAR STRESS**	**31**
	3.1 Surface shear stresses: glued joints	31
	3.2 Internal shear stresses: fastened joints	34
	3.3 Internal shear stresses: punching and twisting	37
4	**STRESSES IN ARBITRARY DIRECTIONS**	**40**
	4.1 Inclined planes and force components	40
	4.2 Transforming uniaxial stress	43
5	**DESCRIBING STRESS IN TWO DIMENSIONS**	**49**
	5.1 Plane stress	51
	5.2 Sign convention and stress components	53
	5.3 Transforming plane stress	55
6	**PRINCIPAL STRESSES**	**62**
7	**MOHR'S CIRCLE**	**67**
	7.1 Using Mohr's circle 1: extreme stresses	71
	7.2 Using Mohr's circle 2: stresses in other directions	75
8	**THE STRESS TENSOR: DESCRIBING STRESS IN THREE DIMENSIONS**	**78**
9	**SUMMARY**	**83**
	LEARNING OUTCOMES	**84**
	ANSWERS TO EXERCISES	**85**
	ANSWERS TO SELF-ASSESSMENT QUESTIONS	**93**
	ACKNOWLEDGEMENTS	**99**

1 THE CONCEPT OF STRESS

Components and structures, from bolts to bridges, are designed to resist any external forces, called *loads*, that might be exerted upon them during their normal working lives. These can arise from a variety of sources and may be constant or varying. Engineers usually consider external forces to be those whose action originates from outside the structure itself, so this includes the force due to gravity. In the case of a large road or rail bridge, for example, steady long-term loads arise owing to the weight of the structure and any other non-moving parts, such as tollbooths and signal gantries, that it supports. Such static forces may be supplemented by periodic variable loads caused by vehicles passing over the bridge, by wind driving against the structure, and by rain or snow collecting on it (see Figure 1.1).

However, knowledge of external forces, no matter how complete, is not enough for the purposes of engineering structural analysis. This is because it is the distribution of force *within* each component of the larger structure that is important. Even the lowliest bolt in a bridge suffers from some distortion when a vehicle passes over. This distortion is caused by the *internal* forces within the bolt itself, generated by the *external* loading; the bolt's sole purpose is to bear these forces without failure. We will consider complex structures later, but let's start by attempting to understand the way in which an external force is conveyed internally through the material of an individual structural member.

Take a look at the simple rod component in Figure 1.2(a). This rod is part of the mechanism for controlling the flap on each wing of an aircraft. It is the job of the control rod to pass on a force from one part of the control system to the flap itself. The way it does this is simple: when the control system exerts a force on one end of the rod, the rod exerts a force on the flap at its other end (if you grip a pencil at both ends and then push or pull with one hand you will feel the force in the other hand). This is why I have drawn a *pair* of forces in Figure 1.2(a). For the rod to pull on the flap and hold it in a fixed position this pair of forces must balance, i.e. they must act in opposite directions and have equal magnitudes F (grip that pencil again; to stop it moving one way you have to pull back with an equal and opposite force). Under these conditions, a state of equilibrium is attained that applies to *all* points within the rod.

To illustrate this last point more clearly, consider the control rod as drawn in Figure 1.2(b), which I will again assume has equal and opposite forces acting at its two ends. Now imagine that it is possible to make two cuts in the rod to isolate a slice of material at position P. In order to maintain equilibrium, the forces on each side of this imaginary slice must balance, as shown in Figure 1.2(c), and the forces on the slice must be equal and opposite to those applied to the rod ends. Similarly at position Q (Figure 1.2d), where the cross-sectional area of the rod is different, the same equal and opposite forces are necessary to maintain ☑ **equilibrium** ☑ with the external load. I can go through an identical argument for an imaginary slice of material that is cut through the rod at any point. Furthermore, I can make this slice as small as I like – microscopically small – because the internal forces act down to the atomic level. In this way it is possible to imagine how an external force is 'transmitted' internally along the entire length of a component.

Figure 1.1   Many structures often experience variable or periodic loading: dams are subject to fluctuating forces dependent on reservoir water level, bridge loads vary with density and frequency of the traffic that they carry, and buildings experience daily and seasonal changes in loading due to the weather

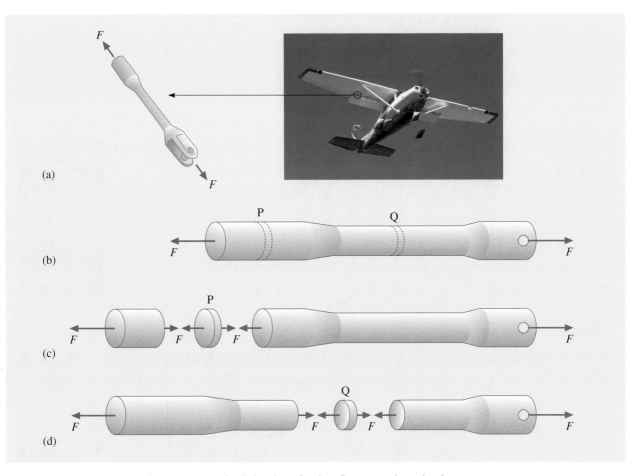

Figure 1.2   Forces in a rod component of a light-aircraft wing-flap control mechanism

☑ Equilibrium and Newton's laws

You will previously have come across Newton's laws of motion. Stated simply, they are:

1   An object will remain at rest or travel with a constant velocity unless a force acts upon it.

2   A net force acting on an object will cause it to accelerate in the direction of the force, at a rate proportional to the magnitude of the force and inversely proportional to the mass of the object.

3   For every action there is an equal and opposite reaction.

In this course we will be concerned with static forces – this is not a dynamics course, although I will have something to say about the effects of variable loading. Equilibrium of forces must apply if an object is stationary: the force pulling on one end of the rod component in Figure 1.2 must equal the force at the other.

This is an expression of the first and third laws: if something isn't accelerating, it's because the forces on it are balanced. So in almost all the cases we look at in this course there will be a balance of forces within the component or structure being studied. This makes things relatively simple.

Now, in the case of the control rod in Figure 1.2 it is also clear that the intensity of the force on the slices at P and Q is different because the cross-sectional areas are not the same. This final point is particularly important, because it is the internal force intensity (the force per unit area) that determines whether or not the material of the rod is capable of supporting a particular load, not simply the magnitude of the external applied forces.

The force intensity is called *stress*, generally denoted by the Greek letter σ (sigma). For a force of magnitude F acting on area A, the average stress over the area is given by:

$$\sigma = \frac{F}{A} \tag{1.1}$$

Using SI units, F is expressed in newtons (N) and A in square metres (m^2), so the units for stress are newtons per square metre ($N\,m^{-2}$), also called a pascal (Pa). For most practical levels of stress in structural materials, $MN\,m^{-2}$ or MPa are commonly used, where M is the prefix 'mega' (i.e. $\times 10^6$).

EXAMPLE

Opposing forces of $F = 800$ N are applied to the ends of part of a wing-flap control rod, identical to that shown in Figure 1.2(b). Estimate the stress on cross sections at both P and Q, where the rod diameters are 8 mm and 5 mm respectively.

SOLUTION

Section P:

The tensile force on the section is 800 N. The stress is:

$$\sigma = \frac{F}{A} = \frac{F}{\pi r^2} = \frac{800\ \text{N}}{\pi \times \left(4 \times 10^{-3}\right)^2 \text{m}^2}$$

$$= 15.9 \times 10^6\ \text{N m}^{-2}$$

$$= 15.9\ \text{MN m}^{-2}$$

$$= 15.9\ \text{MPa}$$

Section Q:

The tensile force is again 800 N, but there is a new cross-sectional area.

The stress at Q is:

$$\sigma = \frac{F}{A} = \frac{F}{\pi r^2}$$

$$= \frac{800\ \text{N}}{\pi \times \left(2.5 \times 10^{-3}\right)^2 \text{m}^2}$$

$$= 40.7\ \text{MPa}$$

Note in the above example that, although the loading stays constant at 800 N, the intensity of the force within the material (i.e. the stress) varies considerably. It is how a material withstands such internal stresses that determines the suitability of a structural component. Also notice from Equation (1.1) that increasing the area by a certain factor will decrease stress by the same factor. In other words, we can say that stress is *inversely proportional* to the area over which it acts. This, in turn, means that stress must be inversely proportional to the square of any linear dimension, such as radius or diameter. These last points will be reinforced if you try Exercise 1.1.

EXERCISE 1.1

Consider again a control rod similar to that shown in Figure 1.2(b).

(a) Calculate the stresses at P and Q if the diameters at these points are *doubled*, to 16 mm and 10 mm respectively, while the applied load remains at 800 N.

Compare these stresses with those calculated in the previous example. What is the proportional change?

(b) What diameters at points P and Q are necessary to create stresses at these sections that are *double* those computed in the previous example (15.9 MPa and 40.7 MPa respectively), for the same applied load of 800 N?

The fact that stress varies with cross section in this way has a fundamental implication for design. If a design engineer wants to reduce the weight of a component by using a smaller section, there will be a higher stress in the component – so there will be a lower failure load during normal use or operation.

2 NORMAL STRESS

When considering the loading of the control rod in Figure 1.2, I was careful to point out that the external loading was applied along the axis of the rod. Such loading is said to be uniaxial, or sometimes just 'axial', because it occurs along one direction or axis only, thus avoiding bending or rotation of the component. This means that the applied force is perpendicular to any transverse cross section that cuts through the rod, as at P and Q in Figure 1.2(b) for example.

In geometry, a 'normal' is a line drawn at right angles to a surface or plane.

In the vocabulary of structures, a 'member' is any piece of a larger structure.

Whenever a force is applied at right angles to an area in this way, the corresponding stress is called a *normal stress*. A normal stress is *tensile* when it acts straight out of a surface, exerting a 'pull', and is *compressive* when it acts straight into a surface, exerting a 'push'. Figure 1.3 shows two structural members loaded at their extremities, one by tensile forces and the other by compressive forces. This external loading creates internal tensile or compressive normal stresses, as illustrated by the slices of material taken at the midsections of each member. As before, these are *imaginary* cuts, intended to illustrate how the internal stresses must balance on an arbitrary piece of material. A real cut would destroy the equilibrium of forces by releasing the internal stresses in the component, and would leave it in two separate pieces.

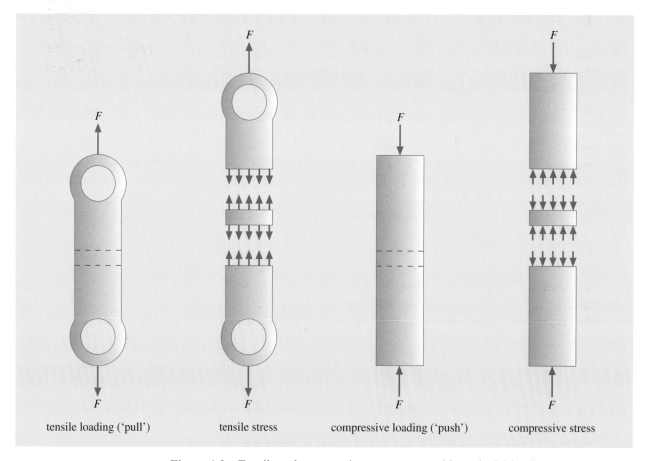

tensile loading ('pull')   tensile stress   compressive loading ('push')   compressive stress

Figure 1.3   Tensile and compressive stresses caused by uniaxial loading

By convention, structural and mechanical engineers assign positive values to tensile stresses and negative values to compressive stresses. This is simply because most, but by no means all, engineering failures occur as a result of excessive tensile stresses, and so it makes sense to have to deal with as few messy minus signs as possible. Geologists and mining engineers, on the other hand, who are more used to dealing with excessive compressive 'overburden' stresses in rocks and soil, do things the other way round – so beware!

The stresses we calculated in the previous example and in Exercise 1.1 were actually average values for the particular plane area. Inside a real body the stress on a given plane may not be uniform everywhere. The variation in stress will depend upon the geometry of the body and the way it is loaded. However, in the case of an axially loaded component of uniform cross section, it can be assumed for practical purposes that the distribution of normal stresses is uniform, except in the immediate vicinity of the points of application of the loads. The fact that stress tends to redistribute itself evenly in this way is a well-known phenomenon called St Venant's principle, named after the French mathematician and engineer Adhémar Jean Claude Barré de Saint-Venant (Figure 1.4), who studied this effect in the latter part of the nineteenth century. Although St Venant drew firm conclusions from his studies of the stress distribution in loaded beams, he was not able to rigorously prove his proposition mathematically – indeed, that was not achieved until almost a century later. Modern engineers tend to be less concerned with mathematical proofs than the usefulness of theories or principles in helping to solve practical problems. On the other hand, it is possible for us to use a very modern numerical modelling tool called ☑ **the finite element method** ☑ to make predictions about ☑ **the distribution of internal stress due to uniaxial loading** ☑ that help us to visualize and validate St Venant's principle.

Figure 1.4   Jean Claude Saint-Venant (1797–1886)

Although uniaxial loading is the simplest type of loading to analyse, it is nevertheless important because an internal uniaxial stress state commonly occurs in many engineering structural components, such as tie bars and rods, loaded along their axis of symmetry. In fact, as you will find out later in this course, many structures are deliberately designed so that uniaxial stresses, either tensile or compressive, dominate. A fuller structural analysis of load-bearing components requires a knowledge of material properties, which we shall come to in Part 2 of this block. For the time being, we can make a simple evaluation of whether an axially loaded component can withstand certain applied loads by assuming, first, that the stress is uniformly distributed within the component, and, second, that the material from which the component is made has a 'maximum allowable' or 'safe working' stress. If this stress is exceeded anywhere within the component, then failure will occur.

☑ The finite element method

The finite element method (often abbreviated to FE method or FEM) aims to tackle a complex numerical problem by dividing it into small parts that are easier to express mathematically. After the larger problem has been broken up and formulated it can then be carefully recombined and solved, usually using a computer. Although finite element analysis is most commonly used by engineers to find out what happens to a structure when a mechanical load is applied to it, there are many other applications. For example, the FEM can be used to predict temperature distributions in a furnace or boiler, fluid flow patterns through valves and pipework, the acoustics of a loudspeaker, or the influence of electromagnetic fields in electrical components such as motors, relays and solenoids.

Whatever the application, the overall strategy is the same. The larger structure is divided up into a number of small blocks, called *finite elements*, which in the case of two-dimensional analysis are usually triangular or quadrilateral shapes; see Figure 1.5(a). These elements are always made to be much smaller than any features of the structure itself and are usually irregular because they need to fit into the larger geometry exactly, without any gaps. All the elements are joined together by their vertices at connecting points called *nodes* (Figure 1.5b). Whereas an element corresponds to a region of material, a node corresponds to a discrete point in space. The entire interconnecting web of elements and nodes is called a *mesh*. Figure 1.5(c) shows a finite element mesh for a tie bar, similar to that considered in Figure 1.3. I created this mesh by asking my finite element modelling software simply to fit about 1000 elements of roughly equal size into the solid geometry of the bar. The software started by arranging elements around the boundaries of the geometry and then worked inwards. This has led to a slightly asymmetric arrangement of elements with some variation in size, particularly near the eyeholes.

The general idea is that if enough elements are used, the continuously varying stress throughout the structure can be approximated into simpler variations within each element. According to its position in the structure, each element is assigned material properties. These properties are used to

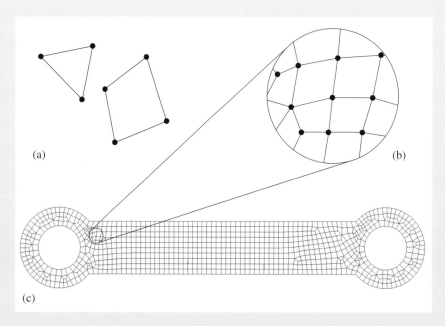

(a)

(b)

(c)

Figure 1.5   (a) Three- and four-sided two-dimensional elements; (b) elements interconnected at nodes; (c) nodes and elements forming a mesh to simulate the more complex geometry of a tie bar

solve, for each element, what is happening within it. Because each node of each element is shared with neighbouring elements, the whole assembly of elements is linked, and the solution arrived at for each element is consistent with those arrived at for all its neighbouring elements. A finite element mesh for a complex engineering structure may consist of many thousands of elements, and a computer is necessary to solve and recombine all these individual problems. Note that the word 'finite' is used here in its mathematical sense to mean 'limited' in size, i.e. neither infinite or infinitesimal. The distinction is important, because shortly you will be introduced to another type of 'element' that *is* infinitesimal, one that is used to describe the stress at a single point in a material. Finite elements are never this small; they are usually made just small enough to be able to interpolate the predicted stress across the structure with acceptable accuracy.

The rapid growth of computing power and data-storage capabilities in recent years has meant that useful finite element analysis, which once required the most sophisticated and expensive computer technology, can now be carried out on a standard desktop machine. Hence it has become an invaluable contemporary tool for the modern structural engineer, and one with which you should at least have some familiarity. During this course you will be introduced to a few of the basic concepts underlying the finite element method and be presented with illustrative examples demonstrating some of its diverse applications in structural analysis. However, I will not teach you how to be a finite element programmer. My aim is to enable you to recognize and interpret finite element results, understand the inputs that go into a finite element model, and for you to gain an appreciation of the uses and limitations of the method. Finite element models can range from the relatively simple, such as the tie bar you have just seen, to the full-scale aircraft simulation shown in Figure 1.6.

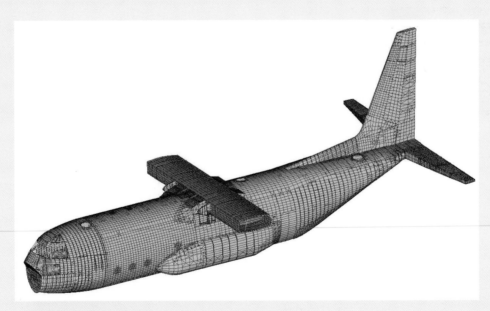

Figure 1.6   Finite element model of the C-130 aircraft

The distribution of internal stresses due to uniaxial loading

When analysing the stress in a structural member under uniaxial loading it is usual to assume that the internal stress distribution is uniform. But how valid is this assumption? And does the uniformity of internal stress depend on the manner in which the load is applied? Take, for example, the simple tensile and compressive loadings illustrated in Figure 1.3. These seem straightforward enough, but the way the load is applied in each case is very different and requires careful consideration. The central section of the tension tie bar is loaded via two circular eyeholes, one at either end, whereas the compression bar is loaded directly at two points on its upper and lower surface.

Let's look at the tie bar first, using the finite element method. This has the advantage of allowing us to 'see' the internal stress distribution throughout the component. I am going to show you the results from an analysis carried out using a mesh identical to that presented in Figure 1.5(c). The tensile loading has been applied to the tie bar via two cylindrical rods that fit into the eyeholes at either end, as shown in Figure 1.7. This has been done to make the loading of the tie bar as 'realistic' as possible; in effect, the applied force is distributed over part of the inner surface of the eyehole, rather than being concentrated at a single point.

In Figure 1.7, contours of predicted stress magnitude have been superimposed upon the mesh in order to make it easy to see the stress distribution. This is the usual way of looking at finite element results. A key is provided that indicates that large tensile stresses are at the red end of the colour scale and compressive stresses are at the blue end. In fact, for this analysis the applied load was chosen such that there ought to be a uniform stress of 50 MPa across the entire central section of the tie bar. The large range of stresses means that this is a little difficult to verify from the colour map alone, although it is clear that much larger localized stresses, up to about 200 MPa in tension and compression, are associated with the loading at the eyeholes.

A more precise assessment of internal stress can be gained from Figure 1.7 by examining the three graphs of stress along different cross sections of the bar. These are taken at distances of $w/4$, $w/2$ and w from the end of one of the eyeholes, where w is the central bar width. It can be seen that the influence of the large local stresses diminishes quickly with distance, so that a reasonably uniform stress of 50 MPa is obtained at a distance of about w from the eyehole.

Although the stress in the main part of the bar is uniform and of the expected magnitude, this is not really a very good design for a tie bar. It would be far better if the extremities of the tie bar were much thicker than the central uniform section and shaped to reduce the concentration of stresses near the point of loading, as illustrated in Figure 1.8. However, because of the larger costs associated with the design and manufacture of more intricate geometries, simpler (but larger) components are often preferred, provided that size and weight is not an overriding issue.

Now let us consider the case of a uniform bar loaded in compression 'at a single point'. This is clearly an artificial means of loading, and is very difficult to achieve in reality without causing local damage to the material (for instance, do not wear stiletto heels on expensive parquet flooring!). So, is there any justification for sketching loading like this, as was presented in Figure 1.3? The results from another finite element analysis, this time carried out on a uniform bar loaded in compression through a single node at the centre of its upper surface, are presented in Figure 1.9. Although the loading is unrealistic, it nevertheless allows us to make a prediction of how quickly highly localized stresses may be redistributed within a structure. The bar is resting on an immoveable plate in order to provide a reaction against the applied load. The width of the bar and the applied load were chosen such that, if the load is distributed evenly, a uniform stress of −50 MPa (compression) should exist within the component. The finite element results indicate, as before, that although local stress is very high immediately beneath the point of loading, the expected uniform stress is achieved within a distance approximately equal to the width of the loaded structure. Note also that there is no noticeable stress concentration associated with the interface between the bar

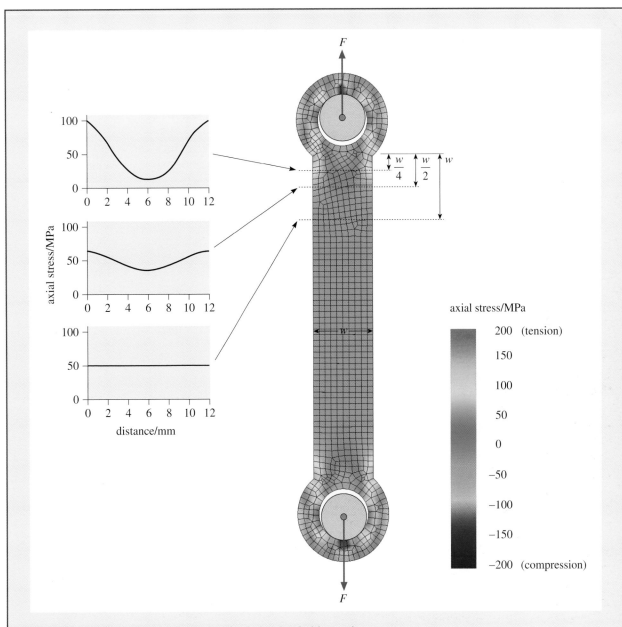

Figure 1.7   Finite element analysis of a tie bar loaded in tension

Figure 1.8   The end of a 'real' tie bar

and the base plate, since the force is evenly transmitted across the entire interface here.

Stated more generally, the conclusions drawn from the results presented in Figure 1.7 and Figure 1.9 indicate that the distribution of stress can be considered uniform outside the immediate region near the application of a load, regardless of the manner in which the load is applied – St Venant's principle again. There is no hard and fast rule concerning

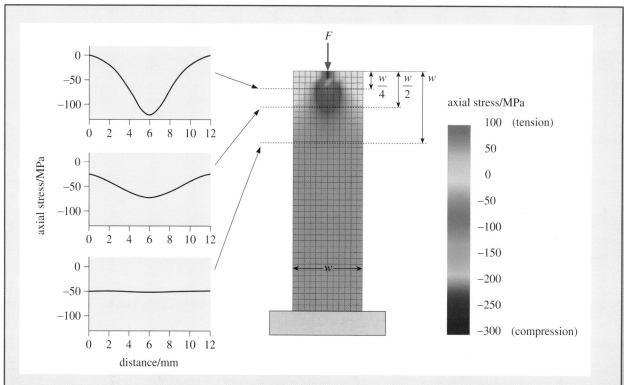

Figure 1.9   Finite element analysis of a uniform bar subject to a concentrated compressive force

the size of the non-uniform stress region near an applied load; but, as you have seen for simple structural bodies, taking it to be the width of the main load-bearing section represents a good rule of thumb. Although somewhat inexact, St Venant's principle is important because it allows engineers to use simple theories, based on average cross-sectional stresses, for the design of many structural members.

EXAMPLE

A tie rod such as that shown in Figure 1.2 carries an axial load of 0.20 MN. If the safe working stress is 200 MPa, estimate the minimum diameter of rod that can be safely used.

SOLUTION

The area associated with the maximum allowable stress can be calculated by rearranging Equation (1.1):

$$A = \frac{F}{\sigma} = \frac{0.20 \times 10^6 \ \text{N}}{200 \times 10^6 \ \text{N m}^{-2}} = 0.001 \ \text{m}^2$$

The corresponding diameter is then deduced by assuming the rod has a circular cross section:

$$A = \pi r^2 = \pi \frac{d^2}{4}$$

Thus:

$$d = \sqrt{\frac{4A}{\pi}} = \sqrt{\frac{4 \times 0.001 \text{ m}^2}{\pi}} = 0.036 \text{ m}$$

Hence the minimum diameter required is 36 mm.

EXERCISE 1.2

A structural member used to support tiered seating in a spectator grandstand has an I-shaped cross section with dimensions as shown in Figure 1.10. If the steel member is designated as having a safe working stress of 250 MPa, estimate the maximum compressive force that the member can withstand when it is loaded uniaxially along its length.

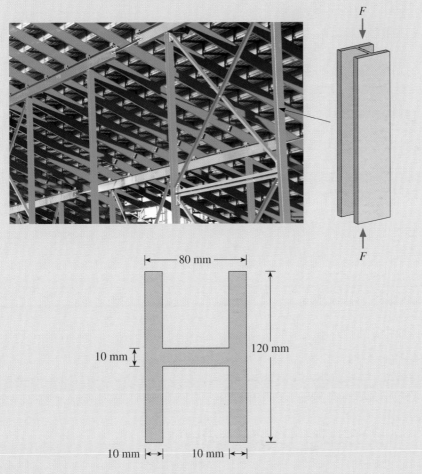

Figure 1.10   Structural I-bar supporting a compressive load

SAQ 1.1 (Learning outcomes 1.1 and 1.2)

A hollow box-shaped column, with dimensions as shown in Figure 1.11, experiences a compressive load of 350 kN along its length when it is used to support part of an overhead walkway.

(a) Estimate the average compressive stress in the material of the column.

(b) If the compressive stress in the column is to be kept below 220 MPa for the same 350 kN load, then a change in the design of the column is necessary. Calculate the new, uniform wall thickness required if the external dimensions of the column are to remain unchanged.

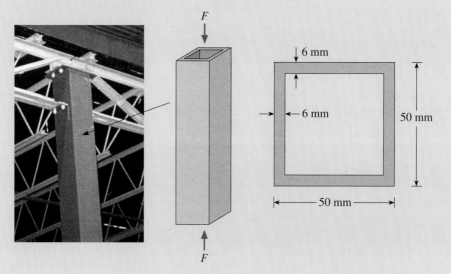

Figure 1.11   Box column supporting a compressive load

3 SHEAR STRESS

The applied forces and corresponding internal stresses we have looked at so far have all been normal (perpendicular) to the cross-sectional area of the material under consideration. However, forces can also act *in the plane* of an area – for example, when a material is cut using a scissor action (see Figure 1.12) – in which case they are called *shear forces*. The analysis of internal shear forces and associated stresses is important because they are usually found anywhere where components are connected together with bolts, pins and rivets; they are also in driveshafts and axles subjected to twisting about their axes, and in many glued joints. Many metal-forming procedures, particularly processes such as cutting and punching, also rely on the development of highly localized internal shear stresses in order to slice through the metal. We will look at how internal shear force is transmitted in all these examples in due course. However, shear is also important in transmitting forces across surfaces. Since this is the simplest case, and the easiest to visualize, it's a good place to start.

3.1 Surface shear stresses: glued joints

Shear forces commonly exist at the interfaces between bonded surfaces. Figure 1.13(a) shows two thin overlapping wooden members that have been adhesively bonded by a layer of glue at their interface. (Throughout this analysis I will assume that the thickness of the adhesive layer is small enough to be ignored in any calculations.) A tensile force F applied parallel to the plane of one of the members sets up a reaction force of the same magnitude in the other member. Because the members are thin we can reasonably assume that the pair of forces acts in approximately the same plane (i.e. they are not significantly offset and so they directly oppose each other). If this were not the case, then there would be a tendency for the offset forces to line themselves up, causing distortion of the joint (which does indeed happen in practice to joints of this type). In Figure 1.13(a) the applied force is effectively transmitted across the joint *via* shear forces at the joint interface. These shear forces must balance the tensile forces applied at the far ends of each member, as illustrated in Figure 1.13(b).

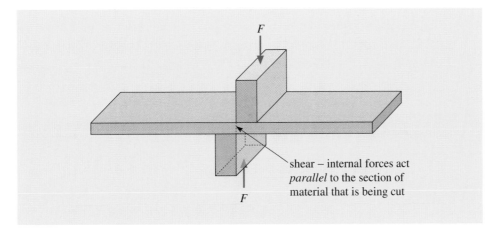

Figure 1.12   In-plane shearing due to scissor-action cutting

Note how I have used half-arrowheads to indicate shear force in this figure, a convention that I will follow throughout the course.

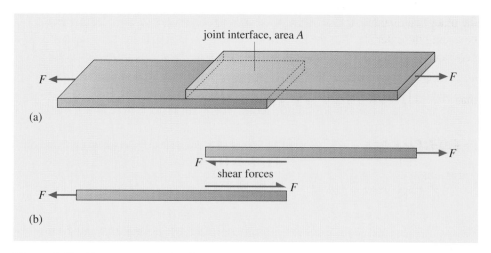

(a)

(b)

Figure 1.13   Forces on a single-shear lap joint

Of course, the integrity of the joint will depend on the intensity of the shear force over the area on which it acts, not on the shear force magnitude alone. Just as a normal force gives rise to a normal stress (normal force per unit area), a shear force induces a shear stress (shear force per unit area). For shear force F, acting over area A, the average shear stress, denoted by the Greek letter τ (tau), is given by:

$$\tau = \frac{F}{A} \tag{1.2}$$

Connections such as that in Figure 1.13, for which the shear stresses are confined to a single plane, are said to be in *single shear*. A connection of this type is often referred to as a *lap joint*, because the members overlap.

In other common joining assemblies two shear surfaces need to be considered, such as for the three-piece wooden glued joint shown in Figure 1.14(a). Here, the tensile load F, applied to the central member, is reacted by a pair of tensile forces of magnitude $F/2$ in

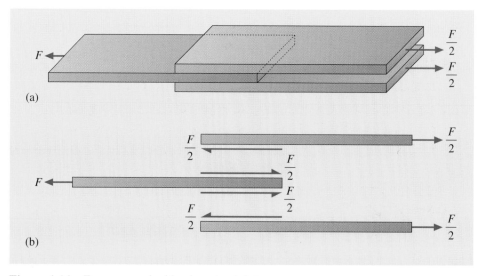

(a)

(b)

Figure 1.14   Forces on a double-shear lap joint

the other two members. Shear forces of magnitude $F/2$ act at the joint interfaces, balancing the external loads, as illustrated in Figure 1.14(b). Hence, shear stresses are generated along a pair of planes and we have a condition known as *double shear*.

The strength of glued joints is usually limited by the strength of the bond itself, rather than that of the material being joined. The following exercise illustrates this.

EXERCISE 1.3

(a) Figures 1.15(a) and (b) show two shear lap joints bonded by an adhesive that has a shear strength of 0.5 MPa. Calculate the maximum tensile loads that can be applied to the ends of each member if the shear strength of the glue is not to be exceeded.

(b) Calculate the tensile load required to break one of the planks shown in Figure 1.15(a), if it has a thickness of 1 mm and a failure stress of 80 MPa.

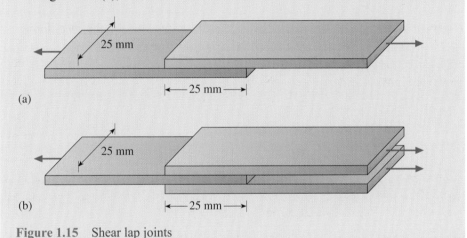

Figure 1.15   Shear lap joints

SAQ 1.2 (Learning outcomes 1.1 and 1.2)

Figure 1.16 shows two wooden planks joined, using thin layers of glue, by plywood splices of length L. The planks, of width 50 mm, are separated by a gap of 10 mm and subjected to tensile loading of 4 kN along their length.

(a) Calculate the shear stress in the glue if the splice length L is 50 mm.

(b) What length do the splices need to be if the maximum allowable shear stress in the adhesive is 1 MPa, assuming the joint width (50 mm) and plank gap (10 mm) remain the same?

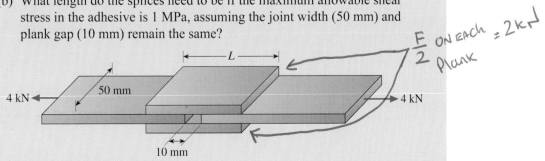

Figure 1.16   Glued wooden joint

3.2 Internal shear stresses: fastened joints

Instead of using adhesives, strong lap joints in metals and other materials are commonly made using fasteners such as ☑ **bolts and rivets** ☑. Such joints can be designed to support predominantly either tensile or shear stresses; here we will concentrate on the latter type of loading.

Take a look at Figure 1.17(a), which shows two thin plates forming a single-shear lap joint, connected by a rivet. As before, a tensile force F acting in the plane of one of the plates creates an opposing reaction force of the same magnitude in the other plate. Ignoring any friction between the plates, this force must be transmitted through the rivet in some way. In fact, the rivet reacts against the forces from the upper and lower plates, as shown in Figure 1.17(b) – that is, there are internal opposing shear forces acting *along* the rivet cross section. To maintain equilibrium, it can be assumed that the average magnitude of the shear force is the same as that of the applied tensile load F.

Similarly, in the case of a bolted double-shear lap joint (Figure 1.18a) the tensile load F applied to the central plate is opposed by tensile forces of magnitude $F/2$ in the other two plates. Within the rivet itself, shear forces of magnitude $F/2$ act along a pair of cross-sectional planes within the bolt, balancing the applied external loads, as shown in Figure 1.18(b).

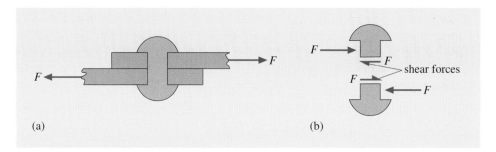

Figure 1.17   Rivet connecting two plates

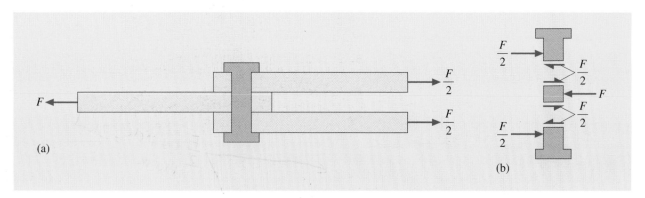

Figure 1.18   Three riveted plates in double shear

☑ Bolts and rivets

Bolting and riveting are, with welding, the most common means of joining bits of metal together (see Figure 1.19). A bolt or rivet acts to clamp together the pieces being joined.

Our analysis of bolted and riveted connections in this section of the course concentrates on those joints which have been specifically designed to resist shear forces. However, you should be aware that other stresses are associated with this type of fixture. This is because the clamping loads on the plates of material they are joining are usually quite high and give the additional benefit of ensuring that there are frictional forces keeping the joint together, as well as the inherent strength of the bolt or rivet.

In a bolted joint, the threaded bolt is inserted into a loose-fitting hole and fixed in place by tightening a nut. This procedure stretches the bolt and so places it in tension; at the same time the joined plates become clamped together and so are in compression. In a riveted joint, a heated rivet is forced into a tight-fitting hole in the connecting plates. After capping the rivet, subsequent cooling and contraction place it in tension and force the plates together in compression. Alternatively, rivets can be fixed using a press that forces the connecting plates together, with the same resulting stress state.

Although, strictly speaking, loose- and tight-fitting fixtures require slightly different analyses, we simply assume they are equivalent – that is, that rivets and bolts completely fill their connecting holes. In both cases the compressive load can create significant friction between the plates that may vary substantially and is difficult to account for. However, ignoring the effect of friction in the analysis of these joints amounts to a conservative estimate of the internal shear stresses. By this I mean that real joints are likely to fail at stresses that are higher than we are predicting. This is because friction acts *against* the applied loads in the plates, thus reducing the effect of the loading. So, by ignoring friction, I am simplifying the calculations and introducing a factor of safety to the answer at the same time.

Fastened connections often involve a number of bolts or rivets arranged symmetrically on either side of the joint. In such cases it can simply be assumed that the applied loads are carried equally by each of the fasteners.

Figure 1.19 Making connections: (a) a bolted plate and (b) workers attaching rivets during construction of the Empire State building

In a fastened connection it is important to remember that the area over which the shear force acts is the cross-sectional area of the rivet or bolt, not the area of the overlapping joined members. This is illustrated by the following example.

EXAMPLE

Figure 1.20 shows two plates joined by a pair of short splice plates and bolts. If the tension across the assembly is 10 kN, what is the average shear stress in bolts C and D, each of diameter 40 mm?

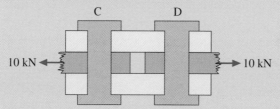

Figure 1.20   Double-bolted connection

SOLUTION

We need to consider only one bolt since, by symmetry, the average shear stress will have the same value in each bolt. By considering the equilibrium of forces (Figure 1.21), bolt C is in double shear and the shear force F along each of the two cross sections is 5.0 kN.

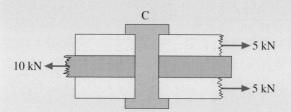

Figure 1.21   Single bolt and forces

The average shear stress on the cross section is:

$$\tau = \frac{F}{A} = \frac{F}{\pi r^2} = \frac{5 \times 10^3 \text{ N}}{\pi \times \left(20 \times 10^{-3}\right)^2 \text{ m}^2} = 4.0 \text{ MPa}$$

EXERCISE 1.4

Part of a structure has been designed such that two thin metal plates are to be joined using a pair of bolts and subjected to tensile loading of 20 kN, as sketched in Figure 1.22. What is the minimum diameter of bolt that you would choose to use in this joint given that the maximum allowable shear stress in the bolt material is 100 MPa, and assuming that the stress will be carried equally by both bolts?

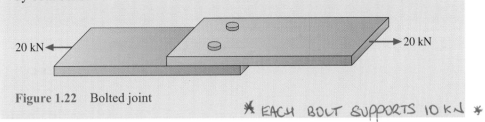

20 kN   20 kN

Figure 1.22   Bolted joint

✷ EACH BOLT SUPPORTS 10 kN ✷

SAQ 1.3 (Learning outcomes 1.1 and 1.2)

An eye bar is attached to a fitting by means of a 25 mm diameter pin (Figure 1.23). What is the maximum force F if the average shear stress in the pin is not to exceed 100 MPa?

Hint: the pin experiences shear forces over two cross sections, so it is in double-shear.

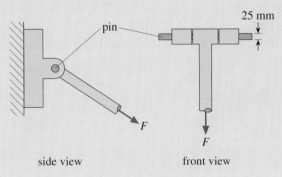

pin

25 mm

F

F

side view   front view

Figure 1.23   Forces on an eye bar

3.3 Internal shear stresses: punching and twisting

So far I have concentrated on lap joints, but internal shear stresses are common in many other types of engineering component and arise during processes such as metal cutting and punching. Consider, for example, a bar of metal that is supported on one side of a flat-sided punch, as illustrated in Figure 1.24(a). If the support is rigid and the applied force is large enough, then it can be assumed that the material of the bar will deform and fail along a single plane. In this case the magnitude of the shear force across the plane is the same as that of the applied load. If the bar is supported on both sides of the punch (Figure 1.24b), then deformation will occur along two planes

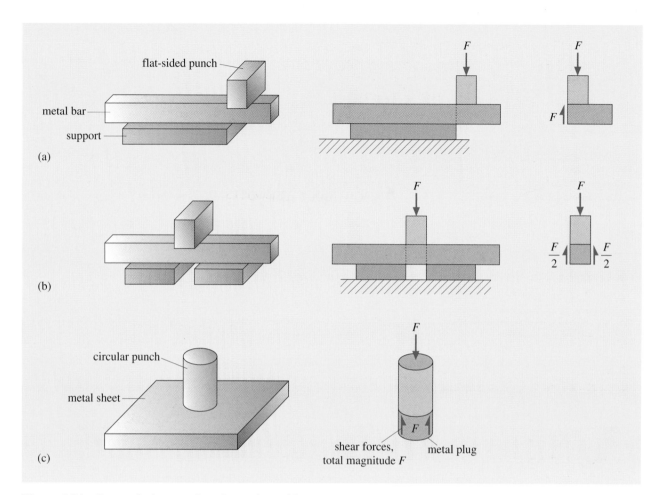

Figure 1.24   Forces during metal cutting and punching

and the shear force along each plane is equal to half the applied force. Similarly, if a square or circular hole is to be cut, then the shear force that reacts against the applied load is distributed across the whole area that is being sheared (Figure 1.24c).

A final, important example involving shear stress is that of a tube or bar subjected to a pair of turning forces that act in opposite directions about its longitudinal axis (Figure 1.25). Such a member is said to be in *torsion*, a stress state that is of particular importance in the axles of wheeled vehicles and in rotating driveshafts used for transferring power in motors and engines. The twisting effect is created by forces that act at a tangent to the circular cross section of the shaft. At equilibrium, the magnitude of the opposing torques must be equal, and within the shaft these must be balanced everywhere by opposing internal shear forces, as sketched in Figure 1.25. However, because the effect of an applied moment is greatest farthest from the axis of rotation, the internal shear forces are not uniform. In fact, they are zero at the centre of a cylindrical bar and reach a maximum at the outer radius – this makes the analysis of stresses in a solid bar subjected to torsion a little tricky. On the other hand, a tube with a thin wall, effectively a tube of fixed radius, can be assumed to have constant shear stress within it. Such a simplification is applicable to the analysis of certain pressure vessels, for example. That is all I want to say about torsion for the time being; however, we will be revisiting this topic in more depth later.

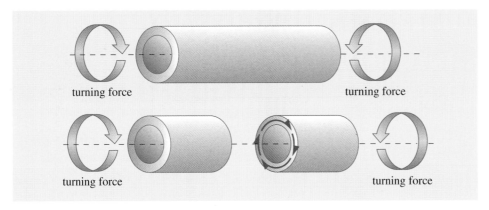

Figure 1.25   Torsion of a hollow shaft

SAQ 1.4 (Learning outcome 1.2)

A sheet of structural steel has a shear strength of approximately 300 MPa. A hole is to be punched in the sheet. Assuming a uniform shear stress on the cylindrical piece of steel that is punched out to make the hole, determine the force necessary to make a 25 mm diameter hole in a plate 10 mm thick. (Think carefully about what area of material is being sheared in this case.)

SAQ 1.5 (Learning outcomes 1.1 and 1.2)

A steel pin, slotted into a hole in an aluminium plate, is supported as shown in Figure 1.26 and subjected to a tensile load of 25 kN. Calculate:

(a) the shear stress in the head of the steel pin caused by the hole in the aluminium plate

(b) the shear stress in the aluminium plate caused by the head of the steel rod.

Hint: the line of action of the internal shear stresses in the pin head and plate are shown as dashed lines in Figure 1.26.

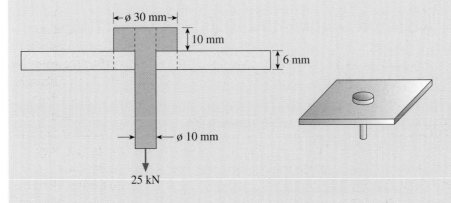

Figure 1.26   Loaded pin and plate

4 STRESSES IN ARBITRARY DIRECTIONS

So far we have considered normal stresses at right angles to the direction of loading and shear stresses parallel to the direction of loading. What about stresses in other directions? Do they exist? Can we calculate them?

Recall the tie bar with eyeholes that we first looked at in Figure 1.3, designed to support a uniaxial tensile load. Our finite element analysis of the entire bar, Figure 1.7, showed uniform stresses in the central section and higher stresses in the vicinity of the eyeholes. But the stresses I plotted in that figure were 'axial' stresses, parallel to the loading aligned along the axis of the specimen (in the 'vertical' direction in the figure). It was no surprise to find stresses in this direction. Now, for each individual element the finite element code also calculates the normal stresses at right angles to this, in the 'horizontal' direction, transverse to the direction of loading in this case. A colour contour map of these transverse stresses, superimposed on the finite element mesh, is shown in Figure 1.27. The transverse stresses at the midsection, more accurately indicated by the graph to the right of the mesh, are indeed zero as expected. However, the colour map clearly indicates that transverse stresses are significant near the eyeholes and at the extremities of the bar. Indeed, they are as great as the axial stresses in these regions. You may find this to be rather unexpected, especially as this is really a very simple structural component. In the case of the tie bar, normal stresses perpendicular to the direction of loading have resulted from localized contact loading in combination with the circular geometry of the eyeholes. But imagine the complex pattern of stresses that might arise, for example, within the intricate geometry of a turbine blade (Figure 1.28) riddled with ventilation holes and centrifugally loaded as it spins at 10 000 rpm to propel hot gas through the chambers of an aero-engine. To assess fully whether the maximum allowable stress might be exceeded in any structural component it is necessary for an engineer to be able to determine the stress in *all* directions within that component. As it turns out, that is not as difficult as you might think.

4.1 Inclined planes and force components

I will start by showing you how to compute stress in an arbitrary direction for a uniaxially loaded member. Figure 1.29(a) shows our now-familiar tie bar, loaded with axial tensile force F, but this time I have drawn a plane section, labelled PQ, at an angle to the direction of loading. To maintain equilibrium this inclined section must experience a vertical force, also of magnitude F, that opposes the applied load. You should realize by now that this internal force is actually distributed across the whole of the section, but it can still be represented by a single force as shown. In fact, this force can, in turn, be represented by two force *components*: a normal force F_n perpendicular to the section and a shear force F_s along the section (Figure 1.29b). If PQ is inclined at an angle θ to the horizontal direction, then,

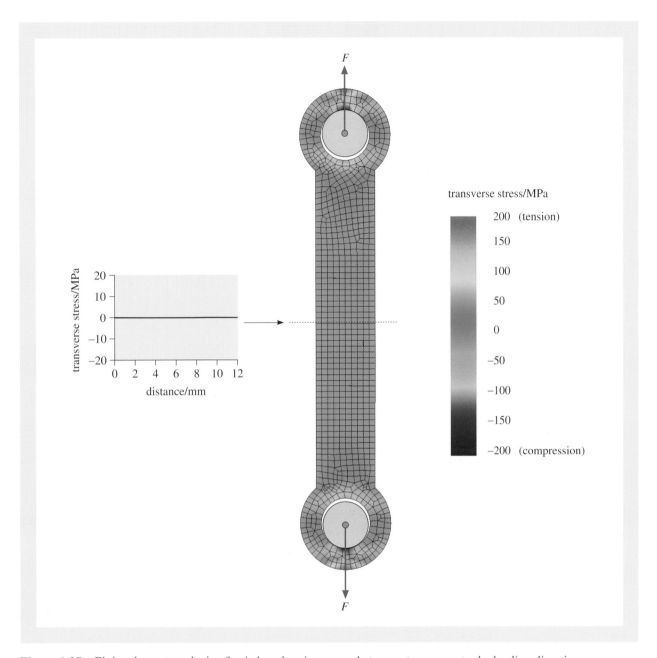

Figure 1.27   Finite element analysis of a tie bar showing normal stresses transverse to the loading direction

by ☑ **resolving the force** ☑ F in these two directions, we have (Figure 1.29c):

$$F_n = F \cos \theta$$
$$F_s = F \sin \theta$$

(1.3)

Note that these internal forces act on the area of the inclined plane, not the horizontal cross-sectional area. To generalize, we can say that a bar in axial tension or compression has both normal and shear force components on inclined sections.

Figure 1.28   Aero-engine turbine blades are subject to centrifugal forces that create essentially uniaxial tensile loading, but the complex blade geometry ensures an equally complex internal stress distribution

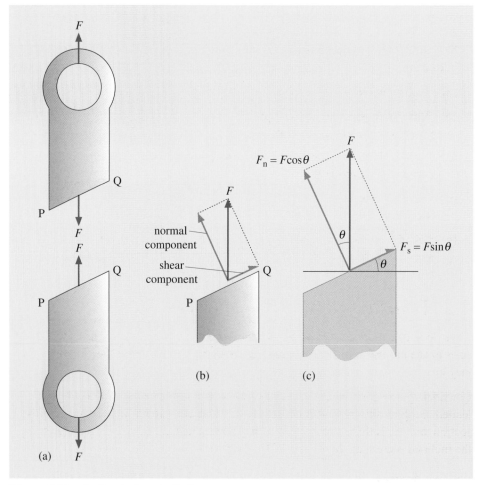

Figure 1.29   Inclined plane in tie bar

☑ Resolving the force

You should know that forces can be 'resolved' to find the component of a force acting along any arbitrary direction, but usually parallel to one of a set of axes that have been chosen for analysing a problem. For the simple case shown in Figure 1.29(c), for a force acting as shown relative to the axes, the resolution is as shown in Equation (1.3). You can work out whether to use sine or cosine by looking at the geometry of the problem, and remembering that, in a right-angled triangle, the sine and cosine of an angle θ can be related to the lengths of the sides of the triangle:

$$\sin\theta = \frac{\text{opposite}}{\text{hypotenuse}} \qquad \cos\theta = \frac{\text{adjacent}}{\text{hypotenuse}}$$

EXERCISE 1.5

Figure 1.30 shows part of a tie bar of rectangular cross section 40 mm × 20 mm. The rod carries a tensile load of 200 kN. Section PQRS is inclined at 30° to the horizontal.

(a) Determine the section area.

(b) What force is exerted by the upper part of the bar on the lower part?

(c) Find the force component perpendicular to the section.

(d) Find the force component along the section.

(e) Calculate the normal and shear stresses on the section.

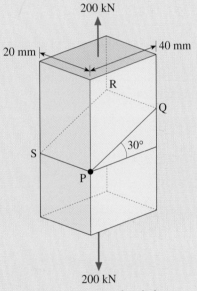

Figure 1.30 Rectangular tie bar

4.2 Transforming uniaxial stress

If we do a little more analysis then we can come to a better understanding of how the sizes of the normal and shear stresses vary with the orientation of the plane on which they act.

Consider again an inclined section, this time within a square bar of side length a loaded along its axis as shown in Figure 1.31. The average normal stress on a cross section, area A, is therefore $\sigma = F/A$, using Equation (1.1). If we denote the area of the inclined section as A_θ (Figure 1.31), we have:

$$A = a \times a$$

$$A_\theta = a \times \frac{a}{\cos\theta} = \frac{A}{\cos\theta} \tag{1.4}$$

Hence, using Equations (1.3) and (1.4), we can write an expression for the normal stress σ_θ on the inclined section:

$$\sigma_\theta = \frac{\text{normal force}}{\text{inclined area}} = \frac{F_n}{A_\theta} = \frac{F\cos\theta}{A/\cos\theta} = \frac{F}{A}\cos^2\theta$$

or, using Equation (1.1):

$$\sigma_\theta = \sigma\cos^2\theta \qquad (1.5)$$

Note that the angle θ between the section and the horizontal direction is the same as that between the direction of the normal stress σ_θ and the applied tensile load (Figure 1.31). For the shear stress τ_θ on the inclined plane we have:

$$\tau_\theta = \frac{\text{shear force}}{\text{inclined area}} = \frac{F_s}{A_\theta} = \frac{F\sin\theta}{A/\cos\theta} = \frac{F}{A}\sin\theta\cos\theta$$

or

$$\tau_\theta = \sigma\sin\theta\cos\theta \qquad (1.6)$$

Equations (1.5) and (1.6) are called 'transformation equations', because they are used to change from an applied axial stress σ to stress components σ_θ and τ_θ on an inclined section. The transformation equations apply to tensile or compressive axial loading provided that the correct sign convention is used (tension positive, compression negative).

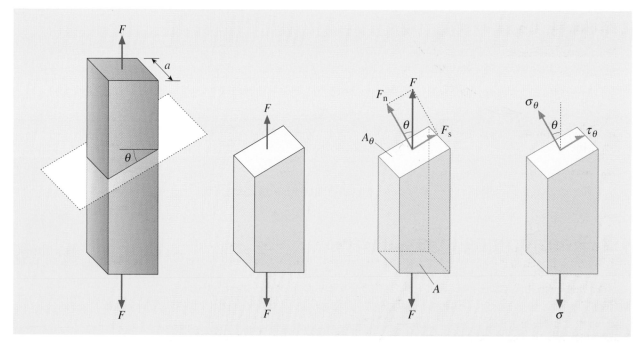

Figure 1.31   Forces and stresses on an inclined section through a square bar

EXAMPLE

A bar, forming part of a heavy press and having a square cross section of side 50 mm, is loaded in tension by uniformly distributed forces of total magnitude 50 kN at each end (Figure 1.32). Determine the stress components on a section inclined at 30° to the direction of loading.

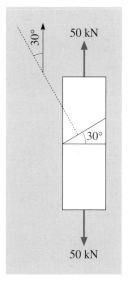

Figure 1.32   Square bar under tensile loading

SOLUTION

Cross-sectional area, $A = 2500 \times 10^{-6} \text{ m}^2$

Force, $F = 50 \times 10^3 \text{ N}$

Axial stress, $\sigma = F/A = 20.0 \text{ MPa}$

Stress components on the inclined section:

average normal stress,

$$\sigma_\theta = \sigma \cos^2 \theta = 20.0 \text{ MPa} \times (\cos 30°)^2 = 15.0 \text{ MPa}$$

average shear stress,

$$\tau_\theta = \sigma \sin \theta \cos \theta = 20.0 \text{ MPa} \times \sin 30° \times \cos 30° = 8.7 \text{ MPa}$$

EXERCISE 1.6

For the bar in Figure 1.32, calculate the stresses on inclined sections at 15°, 45°, 75° and 90° to the loading direction and complete Table 1.1.

Table 1.1   Stresses on inclined sections of a square bar under tensile loading

Angle of section, θ	0°	15°	30°	45°	60°	75°	90°
σ_θ/MPa	20.0		15.0		5.0		
τ_θ/MPa	0		8.7		8.7		

EXERCISE 1.7

From the solution to Exercise 1.6 you have a table of stress components on different inclined sections of a bar under uniaxial stress, with $\sigma = 20.0$ MPa.

Use these data to plot a graph of σ_θ against θ and τ_θ against θ on the same set of axes. In this case I have provided a graph grid for you (Figure 1.33), but you will need graph paper for the later questions in this section. Put stress on the vertical axis and θ on the horizontal axis. Join the data points to make two smooth curves and answer the following questions:

(a) Which section experiences the maximum normal stress?

(b) Which section experiences the maximum shear stress?

(c) Which sections have zero shear stress?

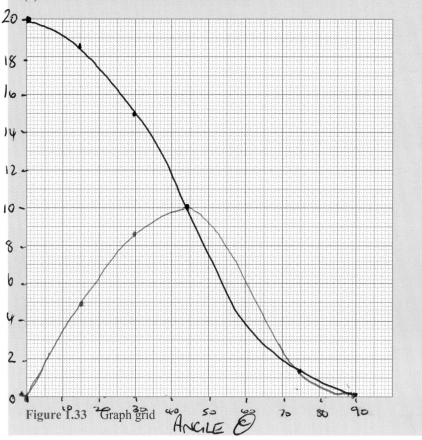

shear stress

normal stress

Figure 1.33 Graph grid

ANGLE θ

You can confirm the findings you made graphically in Exercise 1.7 by inspecting Equations (1.5) and (1.6) more closely. From Equation (1.5) it is clear that the size of normal stress across an internal section under axial loading varies with the quantity $\cos^2\theta$. The normal stress has its maximum value σ_{max} at $\theta = 0°$ when the section is perpendicular to the applied load. This is when $\cos\theta$ is also at its maximum, i.e. $\cos 0° = 1$. Hence:

$$\sigma_{max} = \sigma \cos^2 0° = \sigma$$

Similarly, $\sigma_\theta = 0$ when $\theta = 90°$ and $\cos\theta = 0$. Equation (1.6) indicates that the magnitude of the shear stress on the section is determined by the angular variation of the quantity $\sin\theta\cos\theta$. Hence $\tau_\theta = 0$ when either $\theta = 0°$ or $\theta = 90°$, and reaches a maximum value τ_{max} halfway in between, at $\theta = 45°$:

$$\tau_{max} = \sigma \sin 45° \cos 45° = \sigma \times \frac{1}{\sqrt{2}} \times \frac{1}{\sqrt{2}} = \frac{\sigma}{2}$$

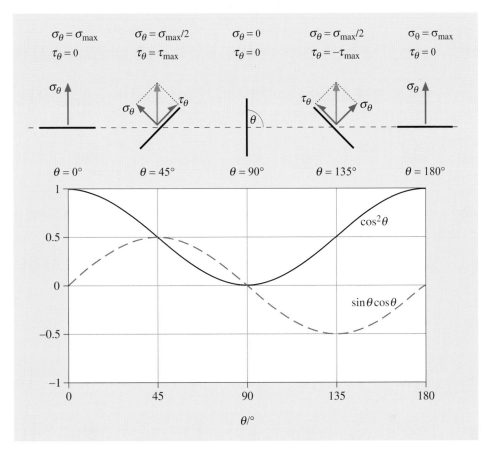

Figure 1.34   Relationships between the orientation of an imaginary plane through a body subjected to uniaxial tension and the magnitudes of the shear and normal stresses that act on the upper face of the plane. Orientation angle θ is measured anticlockwise from the horizontal

Figure 1.34 shows exactly how the normal and shear stresses vary on the upper face of an imaginary plane as it is rotated through a full 180°. Notice that when angle θ is greater than 90°, the function $\sin\theta\cos\theta$ becomes negative and the direction of the shear stress on the section reverses (at $\theta = 45°$ the shear stress τ_θ points to the right of the outward normal stress σ_θ; at $\theta = 135°$ it points to the left). Hence, the sign of the shear stress magnitude is important, because it tells us about its direction, just as the sign of a normal stress tells us whether it is tensile or compressive. I will come back to this in Section 5.2.

You can probably appreciate that, for the purposes of stress analysis, it would be nice to have a simple graphical means of interpreting the variation of stresses with orientation within a structural member. You are also likely to appreciate that Figure 1.34 does not quite fit that description! As it turns out, there is a far more elegant way of plotting these data, as demonstrated by Exercise 1.8.

EXERCISE 1.8

Use again the data derived from the solution of Exercise 1.6, this time to plot a graph of τ_θ against σ_θ. Put τ_θ on the vertical axis and σ_θ on the horizontal axis, using the same scale on both axes. Join the points using a smooth curve. Does the curve approximate some geometrical figure?

Exercise 1.8 shows something rather interesting about plotting the variation between τ_θ and σ_θ. Your curve should have looked semicircular. Actually, the curve is a full circle if values of θ from 0° to 180° are plotted, and circles of this type are a widely used method of visualizing and interpreting internal stresses, as you will find out in Section 7 Mohr's circle.

5 DESCRIBING STRESS IN TWO DIMENSIONS

We have looked at how normal and shear stresses are generated within a material subjected to loading in a single direction only. I now want to turn your attention to the more general two-dimensional case, for which loading is still in one plane but no longer confined to a single direction. Engineers describe loading that is applied in more than one direction at the same time as 'complex' loading. That is not to say that the going is now going to get difficult, but it will become necessary to be more careful and systematic about how we depict stresses and the directions in which they act.

EXERCISE 1.9

Can you identify, from your own experience, some components that experience more than one load, acting in different directions?

First of all, I want you to turn your attention to *where* a stress is acting. We have already seen how the stresses vary with position in something like a tie bar. The calculations we have performed have assumed that the stress is constant over a relatively large internal area, often covering the entire cross section of a structural member. This is fine in regions where we know that the stress changes little, but what area would we use around the loading point of a tie bar?

The practical approach is to choose a hypothetical piece of material, within a larger body, that is small enough so that the stresses acting over it are essentially uniform. In fact, in stress analysis it is conventional to consider how internal stresses act on very small blocks of material, called *elements*. These stress elements are much smaller than the ones used in finite element analysis; in fact, they are *infinitesimally* small, so that they allow us to describe the stress state at a single point. They allow us not only to describe the combination of stresses that act at a point, but also help describe how these might vary with orientation. Take a look at ☑ **Describing stress at a point** ☑ to see how this works. From now on, I am going to stop making imaginary cuts through things in order to reveal the internal stresses. Rather, I will use small elements across which the uniform shear and normal stresses are balanced.

Now, to describe the stress state in a body unambiguously it is useful to impose a fixed coordinate system as a means of reference. This is better than referring to the geometry or symmetry of the body itself, which may change if it deforms or rotates, and is preferable to applying arbitrary descriptions such as 'vertical' and 'horizontal'. Here, I will choose to use an *xy*-coordinate system with the *x*-axis parallel to what I have previously called the 'horizontal' direction and the *y*-axis in the 'vertical' direction. Once a coordinate system has been defined with respect to a particular element, it is possible to describe positive and negative directions and planes with respect to this system, as shown in Figure 1.37. Note from this figure that the *xy*-coordinate system is actually part of a full three-dimensional *xyz*-coordinate

☑ Describing stress at a point

It is usual to describe the stress state in a body using tiny blocks of material, called elements, which are small enough for the stresses within them to be considered uniform. For a full three-dimensional analysis, stress elements need to be cubes, but when considering stress in two dimensions we can simply use square elements, representing one face of the cube (this is completely different from the finite element method, where many different shapes and volumes are used). Figure 1.35(a) shows two such elements, drawn large for clarity, within a tie rod that has been loaded in uniaxial tension. If we choose the element aligned with the rod axis (Figure 1.35b), then we find that it has equal normal stresses top and bottom, zero normal stresses on the sides, and zero shear stresses all round. However, if we choose an element inclined at an angle (Figure 1.35c), then, because the faces are inclined, we can expect there to be normal and shear stresses on all the faces.

Now, consider the stresses on the inclined element a little more carefully. Note that I have drawn pairs of normal stresses of equal magnitude on opposite faces, labelled as σ_a and σ_b; and likewise for the shear stresses, τ_a and τ_b. Were they to act alone, each normal stress would cause *translation* (i.e. motion in the direction along which the stress was acting) of the element, whereas the shear stresses would cause *rotation*. If the tie bar is successfully carrying applied loads and is not accelerating, then the element is in equilibrium and, because the loads act on equal areas of the uniform element, the translational and rotational stresses should balance. Clearly, such a balance is satisfied by opposing normal stresses of equal magnitude. But what about the shear stresses? In Figure 1.35(c) the shear stresses labelled τ_a tend to cause the element to rotate anticlockwise, whereas those labelled τ_b act to rotate it clockwise. The only way these two pairs of shear stresses can balance is if they are of equal magnitude (i.e. if $\tau_a = \tau_b$). This is an important result that applies generally: the shear stresses on intersecting perpendicular planes (i.e. the faces of our square element) must always be equal in magnitude. These are called *complementary shear stresses*. Hence, the element of Figure 1.35(c) can be redrawn as in Figure 1.36, which is the usual way of drawing an equilibrium element describing the stress state at a single point.

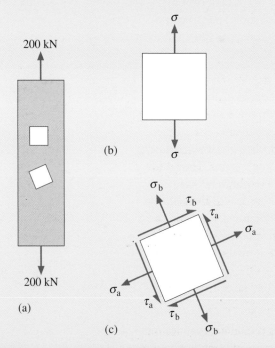

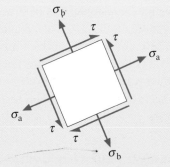

Figure 1.35   (a) Tie bar with two-dimensional elements; (b) vertically aligned element showing normal stresses; (c) inclined element showing normal and shear stresses

Figure 1.36   Element with complementary shear stresses

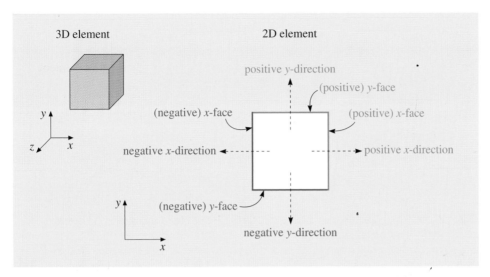

Figure 1.37 Directions and sides of a two-dimensional element defined with respect to an *xy*-coordinate system. Note that the element faces are named after the axes to which they are perpendicular

system, with the *z*-axis directed out of the page towards you. In fact, the two-dimensional element in Figure 1.37 can be considered as a 'side view' (looking in the negative *z*-axis direction) of the three-dimensional one.

5.1 Plane stress

The two-dimensional approach to stress analysis I have just introduced assumes that all the stresses occur in a single plane; there are no shear or normal stresses acting on the *z*-faces of the three-dimensional element sketched in Figure 1.37. This is known as a state of *plane stress* (sometimes just called two-dimensional stress) and is a simplification that is widely adopted in engineering analysis. At first sight it may seem appropriate only for perhaps a flat plate with stresses on the edges parallel to the plane of the plate. It is possible, however, to extend the application of the plane stress model to components or bodies that are relatively thin in relation to their other dimensions. In such bodies it is difficult to generate stresses through a small thickness, and all the stresses parallel to the thickness direction (i.e. along the *z*-axis) can be assumed to be zero. Plane stress is also useful in modelling the stress pattern at or near the surface of a fully three-dimensional body. This is because stress cannot be transmitted across open space, so the normal stress at a 'free' surface must be zero, and only the stresses in the plane of the surface need be considered.

To describe a state of plane stress it is helpful to use a notation that incorporates our chosen coordinate system. For normal stresses this can be achieved using a single subscript: normal stresses in the *x*- and *y*-directions, regardless of whether they are positive or negative, are written as σ_x and σ_y respectively (Figure 1.38a). To describe shear stress it is necessary to use two subscripts. The first subscript indicates the *plane* (i.e. the element face) on which the shear stress acts, and the second subscript

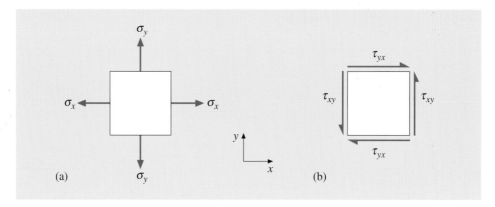

Figure 1.38   Notation used in two-dimensional, plane stress analysis: (a) normal stresses; (b) shear stresses

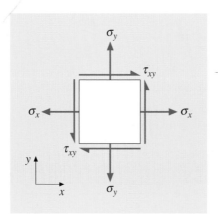

Figure 1.39   Plane stress element subjected to general stress

refers to the *direction* of the shear stress. Planes or faces are named after the axis to which they are perpendicular, as indicated in Figure 1.37. Hence, referring to Figure 1.38(b), τ_{xy} is the shear stress on the plane perpendicular to the *x*-axis (the element *x*-face) and in a direction parallel to the *y*-axis. Similarly, τ_{yx} is the shear stress on the plane perpendicular to the *y*-direction (the element *y*-face) and acting parallel to the direction of the *x*-axis. For a two-dimensional element of material in equilibrium we have $\tau_{xy} = \tau_{yx}$, and so only three stresses, σ_x, σ_y and τ_{xy} are necessary to describe a state of plane stress fully – see Figure 1.39, although, of course, one or more of these may be zero.

As I have already mentioned, plane stress is sufficient in practice for the analysis of a great many real engineering situations, several of which you have met previously. For example, Figure 1.40(a) shows an element in a column under *uniaxial* stress, compression in this case, oriented parallel to the *y*-axis. Figure 1.40(b) shows an element that experiences normal stresses in *both* the *x*- and *y*-directions. This state of stress is called *biaxial* stress and arises, for example, in a sheet of material that is loaded in perpendicular directions – such as in the walls of a thin pressurized vessel or balloon. Figure 1.40(c) shows another type of two-dimensional loading in which an element is subjected to shear stresses only. This is a state of *pure shear* stress, which can occur, for example, in shafts under torsion. Note that uniaxial stress, biaxial stress and pure shear stress are all special cases of plane stress.

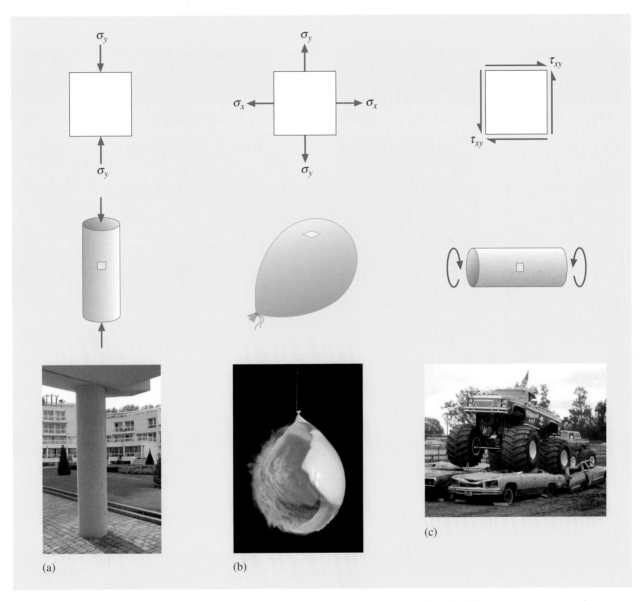

Figure 1.40   Stress states common in two-dimensional engineering analysis: (a) uniaxial stress, e.g. structural support column loaded in compression; (b) biaxial stress, e.g. in the stretched thin skin of a pressurized balloon; (c) pure shear, e.g. as a result of opposing turning forces acting on the axle of a truck

5.2 Sign convention and stress components

I now want you to think a little bit more about how the stresses have been drawn for the plane stress element in Figure 1.39. It is clear that the normal stresses are tensile because they have been drawn pointing outwards from the sides of the element. I mentioned earlier that, by convention, most engineers take tensile stresses to be positive and compressive stresses to be negative. Hence if I told you, for example, that one of the normal stresses on an element was equal to −25 MPa you would draw it pointing inwards, indicating compression. But how would you draw a shear stress of −25 MPa? The answer, of course, is that you can do this only once a sign convention for shear stresses has also been established. In fact, I have chosen one and have been using it already: *a shear stress is positive if it acts in the positive direction on the positive face of an element.* (The positive and negative faces of an element were defined in Figure 1.37.) Similarly, a shear stress is also positive if it points in the negative direction on the negative side of the element; all other shear stresses are negative. Look carefully at the stresses in Figure 1.39 again. Using my chosen sign convention, I have drawn all the stresses in this figure so that they are positive.

EXAMPLE

Figure 1.41 shows an equilibrium plane stress element with the direction and magnitude (in MPa) of the normal and shear stresses indicated. Write down the stress components using the sign convention described above.

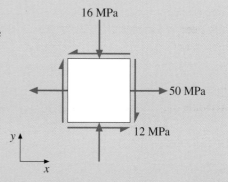

Figure 1.41   Example plane stress element

SOLUTION

Normal stress in the *x*-direction points out of the element (tension), hence $\sigma_x = 50$ MPa.

Normal stress in the *y*-direction points into the element (compression), hence $\sigma_y = -16$ MPa.

Shear stress acts in negative directions on positive planes, hence $\tau_{xy} = -12$ MPa.

EXERCISE 1.10

Write down the stress components for the element of Figure 1.42 using the sign convention described above.

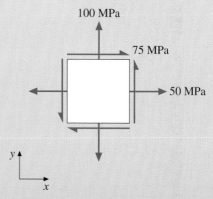

Figure 1.42   Plane stress element

EXERCISE 1.11

Sketch two-dimensional elements for the following stress states:

(a) Biaxial stress with $\sigma_x = 150$ MPa and $\sigma_y = -100$ MPa.

(b) Pure shear stress of −50 MPa.

(c) $\sigma_x = 40$ MPa, $\sigma_y = -20$ MPa and $\tau_{xy} = -20$ MPa.

5.3 Transforming plane stress

To carry out a stress analysis of a structural member under a particular loading condition we can start by choosing an element of material at some point of interest, and then determine the stresses on that element. These can be deduced from a knowledge of the applied loads and the geometry of the component, or they can be calculated using ▽ **strain gauges** ▽ bonded to the surface of the structure, as you will see in more detail in Block 1 Part 2. Whatever method we choose, it is likely that we will have a set of stresses only for one particular orientation of the element at that point. But what we really need is a means of assessing the stress in *all* directions, so that we can determine which set of stresses is the largest – that is, those most likely to cause failure.

So far I have arranged the generalized plane stress element so that its sides are aligned with the normal stresses oriented in the *x*- and *y*-directions. In order to determine the stresses in a different direction, on an inclined section of this element

▽ Strain gauges

When testing materials and components, it is often necessary to be able to measure the deflection or extension of a component or test-piece. There are ways to do this involving clamping transducers to the surface or using non-contact optical methods, but one of the simplest and cheapest methods is the use of strain gauges.

Typically, a strain gauge is made from a long, thin strip of metal arranged in a zigzag shape, attached to an insulating, plastic mount (see Figure 1.43).

The gauge is glued onto the component surface; any changes in strain at the surface will then cause small, but measurable, changes in the resistance of the wire. The resistivity does not change much, but the length and the area do, particularly as there is quite a significant length of metal coiled in the gauge.

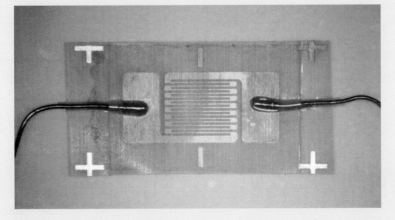

Figure 1.43   A strain gauge

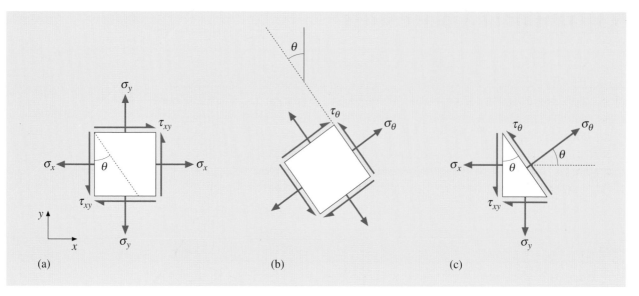

(a)   (b)   (c)

Figure 1.44   Determination of stresses on an inclined section of a plane stress element. (a) The general element with an inclined section (dashed line) defining an internal triangular element; (b) the general element rotated through θ degrees; (c) the triangular element redrawn to show the stresses acting on it

(the dashed line in Figure 1.44a), it is necessary to use transformation equations of the type we derived in Section 4.2 for uniaxial stress. Note that determining the stresses on the inclined plane in Figure 1.44(a) is the same as rotating the initial element anticlockwise through angle θ and then determining the stresses on the side that was originally perpendicular to the positive x-direction (Figure 1.44b). The precise derivation of the plane stress transformation equations is a rather lengthy exercise in trigonometry and not really necessary for current purposes. It is sufficient to point out that determining the equations can be done by considering the equilibrium of forces on the triangular element shown in Figure 1.44(c), part of the square element of Figure 1.44(a). The final transformation equations for plane stress contain more terms than those for uniaxial stress, Equations (1.5) and (1.6), because the stress components on the inclined section, σ_θ and τ_θ, are now related to the stresses σ_x, σ_y and τ_{xy} rather than just to a single uniaxial stress σ. The transformation equations for plane stress are:

$$\sigma_\theta = \frac{1}{2}\left(\sigma_x + \sigma_y\right) + \frac{1}{2}\left(\sigma_x - \sigma_y\right)\cos 2\theta + \tau_{xy}\sin 2\theta \tag{1.7}$$

$$\tau_\theta = -\frac{1}{2}\left(\sigma_x - \sigma_y\right)\sin 2\theta + \tau_{xy}\cos 2\theta \tag{1.8}$$

where θ is the angle between σ_θ (the normal to the inclined plane) and the x-axis, measured in the anticlockwise direction – see Figure 1.44(c). The direction in which the angle is measured is important, as explained in ☑ **A cautionary note about stress transformation equations** ☑.

☑ A cautionary note about stress transformation equations

The transformation Equations (1.7) and (1.8) work provided you follow the sign convention for shear and normal stresses presented in Section 5.2, and assume that the angle θ is positive when it is measured anticlockwise from the positive x-direction. Other textbooks can take a different approach that, if followed systematically, will give correct results. However, these often require the use of transformation equations that are slightly different from those presented here. In such cases some of the positive and negative signs are transposed. Always ensure that you are familiar with the appropriate sign convention – the directions of the axes and which way the angles are measured – when applying formulae from another source to analyse complex stress states.

Complex states of stress commonly occur within the walls of pressurized containers such as diving cylinders (scuba tanks), compressed-air receivers and liquefied-gas storage tanks (Figure 1.45). Pressure vessels of this type are usually based on a cylindrical design, and the internal pressure tends to create large tensile stresses in the container walls that are similar in origin to the stresses that arise in the stretched balloon skin of Figure 1.40(b). However, this biaxial tensile stress field is modified by the presence of geometrical complexities, such as inlet and outlet holes, lifting lugs and other attachments, as well as by the weight of the vessel itself. These influences mean that a significant shear stress may also be present. We can analyse the state of stress at the surface of these containers by adopting the plane stress assumption.

Figure 1.45   Cylindrical containers for storing pressurized fluids can be found on almost any industrial site

EXAMPLE

Figure 1.46 shows the state of stress at a particular point on the surface of a large, cylindrical pressure vessel. Note that the stress state is one of combined biaxial tension and shear. Calculate the shear and normal stresses on an element at the same point, but rotated through an anticlockwise angle of 45°.

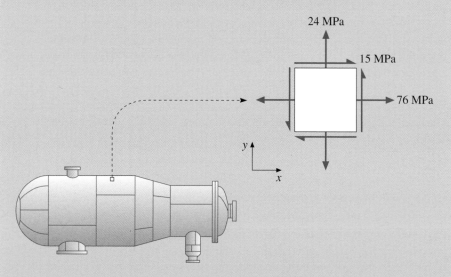

Figure 1.46   Plane stress element at the surface of a pressure vessel

SOLUTION

To determine the stresses on the entire element after it has been rotated we actually just need to find the stresses on *two* adjacent sides of the rotated element, such as those drawn bold in Figure 1.47. All the other stresses can be inferred by symmetry. To use the plane stress transformation equations we must be careful to identify the appropriate faces using the anticlockwise angle between their normals and the direction of the *x*-axis, as indicated in Figure 1.47. In this case, it is necessary to compute the stresses on planes for which $\theta = 45°$ and $\theta = 45° + 90° = 135°$. Note that by rotating the element we are *not* altering the stress state; we are simply changing the directions in which we look at the stress.

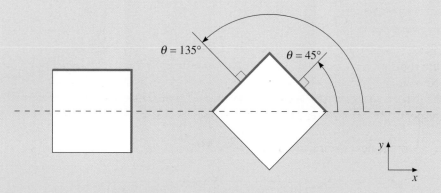

Figure 1.47   Orientation of faces on a stress element, rotated anticlockwise through 45° with respect to the *x*-axis direction

From the stress element in Figure 1.46 we have:

$\sigma_x = 76$ MPa

$\sigma_y = 24$ MPa

$\tau_{xy} = 15$ MPa.

Hence, for $\theta = 45°$:

$$(\sigma_\theta)_{45} = \frac{1}{2}(\sigma_x + \sigma_y) + \frac{1}{2}(\sigma_x - \sigma_y)\cos 2\theta + \tau_{xy}\sin 2\theta$$

$$= \frac{1}{2}(76 + 24) + \frac{1}{2}(76 - 24)\cos 90° + 15\sin 90°$$

$$= 50 + 0 + 15$$

$$= 65 \text{ MPa}$$

(x normal translated)

$$(\tau_\theta)_{45} = -\frac{1}{2}(\sigma_x - \sigma_y)\sin 2\theta + \tau_{xy}\cos 2\theta$$

$$= -\frac{1}{2}(76 - 24)\sin 90° + 15\cos 90°$$

$$= -26 + 0$$

$$= -26 \text{ MPa}$$

(shear)

and for $\theta = 135°$:

$$(\sigma_\theta)_{135} = \frac{1}{2}(76 + 24) + \frac{1}{2}(76 - 24)\cos 270° + 15\sin 270°$$

$$= 50 + 0 + (-15)$$

$$= 35 \text{ MPa}$$

(y normal translated)

It is not actually necessary to compute the shear stress again, because it must be the same on all sides of the element, i.e. $(\tau_\theta)_{135} = -(\tau_\theta)_{45}$, although recalculating does provide a check, so I will do it anyway:

$$(\tau_\theta)_{135} = -\frac{1}{2}(76 - 24)\sin 270° + 15\cos 270°$$

$$= 26 + 0$$

$$= 26 \text{ MPa}$$

When it comes to sketching the rotated element, pay careful attention to the signs of the stresses, which may have changed. To use our adopted sign convention (Section 5.2) it is necessary to imagine that the x- and y-axes have been rotated with the element so that they now lie in directions x' and y' respectively, as illustrated in Figure 1.48. Hence, for the rotated element:

in the new x'-direction $(\sigma_\theta)_{45} = 65$ MPa

in the new y'-direction $(\sigma_\theta)_{135} = 35$ MPa

shear stress $(\tau_\theta)_{45} = -26$ MPa

and the direction of the shear stress in Figure 1.48 is consistent with it being negative with respect to the x'- and y'-axes.

Finally, note that I could have used *any* pair of adjacent element sides in Figure 1.48 to complete the above analysis. Those for which $\theta = 45°$ and $\theta = 315°$, for example, would have done just as well. I could also use *clockwise* angles provided that I assign them a negative value. $\theta = -45°$ is the same as $\theta = 315°$, for instance. If you are not convinced about this, try it!

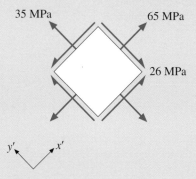

35 MPa   65 MPa

26 MPa

y' x'

Figure 1.48 Rotated element and coordinate system

EXERCISE 1.12

The state of plane stress at a certain point on the upper surface of an aircraft wing during flight is shown in Figure 1.49. The orientation of the stress element has been chosen so that it is aligned with the axis of the fuselage, and in this orientation the stress state is one of combined torsion and uniaxial compression. Calculate and sketch the normal and shear stresses on an element at the same point, but aligned with the front edge of the aircraft wings, representing a rotation of the given element through a clockwise angle of 40°.

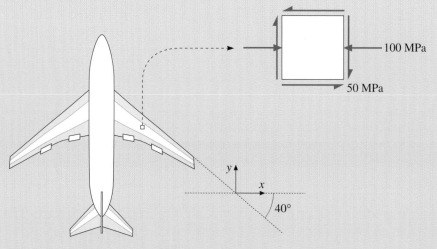

100 MPa

50 MPa

y

x

40°

Figure 1.49 Stress at a point on an aircraft wing

SAQ 1.6 (Learning outcomes 1.3, 1.4 and 1.7)

The state of stress at a point on the surface of a wooden support beam, part of a garden shed, is sketched in Figure 1.50. The direction of the grain of the wood with respect to the known stresses is also shown. Calculate the normal stress perpendicular to the grain and the shear stress parallel to the grain.

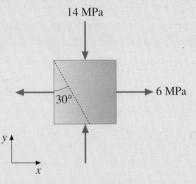

Figure 1.50   Stress state on a wooden beam

6 PRINCIPAL STRESSES

In general, for *any* state of two-dimensional stress at a given point there are two mutually perpendicular planes free of shear stress. These are called the *planes of principal stress*, and the normal stresses which act on them are called the *principal stresses* at the point in question. They are important because they always represent the greatest and least normal stresses that can occur at the point considered. By plotting the variation of σ_θ and τ_θ with θ using Equations (1.7) and (1.8) it is possible to determine the angles at which these limiting stresses occur under general plane stress, just as you did for the special case of uniaxial loading in Exercise 1.6. Without the use of a computer or spreadsheet this is a lengthy calculation, so I have already done this for the last example, concerning the stress state at the surface of a large pressure vessel ($\sigma_x = 76$ MPa, $\sigma_y = 24$ MPa and $\tau_{xy} = 15$ MPa); see Figure 1.51. From Figure 1.51 you should be able to read off that the maximum and minimum normal stresses are $(\sigma_\theta)_{max} = 80$ MPa and $(\sigma_\theta)_{min} = 20$ MPa. These are the principal stresses: the larger (i.e. the most positive or 'more tensile' of the two) is called the *major* principal stress; the other is the *minor* principal stress. In two-dimensional analysis the major and minor principal stresses are usually labelled as σ_1 and σ_2 respectively. You should also notice from Figure 1.51 that the planes on which the principal stresses occur are 90° apart and are the only ones that are not subject to any shear stress. The maximum and minimum shear stresses act on planes oriented at 45° to the principal planes.

To find expressions that allow us to calculate the principal stresses directly it is necessary to set $\tau_\theta = 0$ in Equation (1.8) and then use some complicated trigonometric

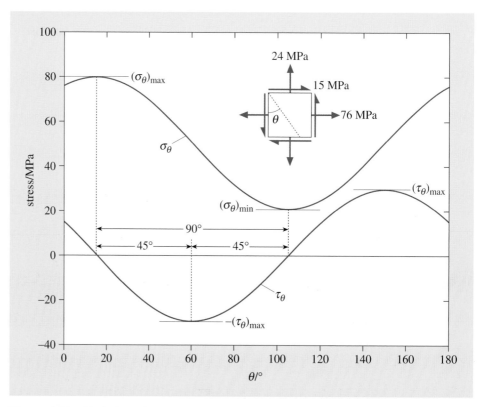

Figure 1.51   Variation of normal and shear stress, σ_θ and τ_θ, with angle θ

expressions to find the maximum and minimum values of the normal stresses. Once again, for stress analysis, we are really interested only in the final result:

$$\left(\sigma_\theta\right)_{\text{max, min}} = \sigma_{1,2} = \frac{\sigma_x + \sigma_y}{2} \pm \sqrt{\left(\frac{\sigma_x - \sigma_y}{2}\right)^2 + \tau_{xy}^2} \tag{1.9}$$

and these stresses occur in directions θ_p given by

$$\tan 2\theta_p = \frac{2\tau_{xy}}{\sigma_x - \sigma_y} \tag{1.10}$$

Here $\left(\sigma_\theta\right)_{\text{max}}$ means 'the maximum value of σ_θ', but I will sometimes use σ_{max} to indicate the maximum stress at a point. They are the same thing.

Because, for any angle, $\tan 2\theta = \tan(180° + 2\theta)$, Equation (1.10) is satisfied by two values of $2\theta_p$ that are 180° apart. In other words, it defines principal stress orientations, θ_{p1} and θ_{p2} that are 90° apart. The problem is that there is no way of knowing which angle, calculated from Equation (1.10), goes with which stress, calculated from Equation (1.9). The thing to do, if you need to know the principal stresses *and* their respective orientations, is to calculate the angles using Equation (1.10), and then compute the principal stresses that correspond with these angles using the transformation Equation (1.7). Just in case that is not clear, the following example shows you how.

EXAMPLE

For the stress state shown in Figure 1.52, calculate the major and minor principal stresses and their respective orientations.

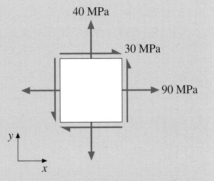

Figure 1.52   Plane stress element

SOLUTION

From the stress element shown in Figure 1.52 we have:

$\sigma_x = 90$ MPa

$\sigma_y = 40$ MPa

$\tau_{xy} = 30$ MPa.

First determine the principal stresses using Equation (1.9):

$$\sigma_{1,2} = \frac{\sigma_x + \sigma_y}{2} \pm \sqrt{\left(\frac{\sigma_x - \sigma_y}{2}\right)^2 + \tau_{xy}^2}$$

$$= \frac{90 + 40}{2} \pm \sqrt{\left(\frac{90 - 40}{2}\right)^2 + 30^2}$$

$$= 65.0 \pm 39.1 \text{ MPa}$$

That is, $\sigma_1 = 104.1$ MPa; $\sigma_2 = 25.9$ MPa.

Next compute the angles from Equation (1.10):

$$\tan 2\theta_p = \frac{2\tau_{xy}}{\sigma_x - \sigma_y} = \frac{(2 \times 30)\ \text{MPa}}{(90 - 40)\ \text{MPa}} = \frac{60}{50} = 1.2$$

$$2\theta_p = \arctan(1.2) = 50.2° \text{ or } 230.2°, \text{ i.e. } 50.2° \text{ or } (50.2 + 180)°$$

$$\theta_p = 25.1 \text{ or } 115.1$$

Finally, insert one of these angles, say $\theta_p = 25.1°$, into Equation (1.7) to find the corresponding stress:

$$\left(\sigma_p\right)_{25.1} = \frac{1}{2}\left(\sigma_x + \sigma_y\right) + \frac{1}{2}\left(\sigma_x - \sigma_y\right)\cos 2\theta + \tau_{xy}\sin 2\theta$$

$$= \frac{1}{2}(90 + 40) + \frac{1}{2}(90 - 40)\cos(50.2°) + 30\sin(50.2°)$$

$$= 65 + (25 \times 0.640) + (30 \times 0.768)$$

$$= 104.1\,\text{MPa}$$

which turns out to be the same as σ_1.

Hence, the major principal stress is $\sigma_1 = 104$ MPa at $\theta_p = 25°$, and the minor principal stress is $\sigma_2 = 26$ MPa at $\theta_p = 115°$.

Similarly, the corresponding maximum shear stress is found by differentiating and manipulating Equation (1.8), with the result:

$$\left(\tau_\theta\right)_{\max} = \pm\sqrt{\left(\frac{\sigma_x - \sigma_y}{2}\right)^2 + \tau_{xy}^2} \tag{1.11}$$

and the angles θ_s in which these shear stresses act are given by:

$$\tan 2\theta_s = -\frac{\sigma_x - \sigma_y}{2\tau_{xy}} \tag{1.12}$$

which again has two solutions. Equation (1.11) generates two values of shear stress that are equal in magnitude but opposite in sign. These are usually both referred to as 'maximum' shear stresses, i.e. as $\pm\left(\tau_\theta\right)_{\max}$, since the sign merely differentiates the direction of the shearing, not the nature of the stress itself. Because complementary shear stresses have the same magnitude on all sides of a two-dimensional element, engineers are often less concerned about specifying which shear stress goes with which plane. However, to determine the correct shear stress orientation we need first to compute the angles from Equation (1.12) and then use the transformation Equation (1.8) to find the sign of the shear stress, just as we did for the principal stresses in the previous example.

EXAMPLE

For the stress state shown in Figure 1.52, determine the maximum shear stress and its orientation.

SOLUTION

From Figure 1.52 we have $\sigma_x = 90$ MPa, $\sigma_y = 40$ MPa and $\tau_{xy} = 30$ MPa. The maximum shear stress can be calculated from Equation (1.11) thus:

$$\left(\tau_\theta \right)_{max} = \pm \sqrt{ \left(\frac{\sigma_x - \sigma_y}{2} \right)^2 + \tau_{xy}^2 } = \pm \sqrt{ \left(\frac{90 - 40}{2} \right)^2 + 30^2 } = \pm 39.1 \, \text{MPa}$$

and the orientation is given by Equation (1.12):

$$\tan 2\theta_s = -\frac{\sigma_x - \sigma_y}{2\tau_{xy}} = -\frac{(90 - 40) \, \text{MPa}}{(2 \times 30) \, \text{MPa}} = -\frac{5}{6}$$

$$2\theta_s = -39.8° \text{ or } 140.2°$$

$$\theta_s = -19.9° \text{ or } 70.1°$$

A negative angle is measured clockwise, so these angles differ from those of the principal stress directions, computed in the previous example, by 45° as expected (see Figure 1.51). Inserting one value of the θ_s angles into Equation (1.8) allows us to determine the sign of the shear stress in that direction:

$$\left(\tau_\theta \right)_{-19.9} = -\frac{1}{2}\left(\sigma_x - \sigma_y \right)\sin 2\theta + \tau_{xy} \cos 2\theta$$

$$= -\frac{1}{2}\left(90 - 40 \right)\sin\left(-39.8° \right) + 30\cos\left(-39.8° \right)$$

$$= -\left(25 \times -0.640 \right) + \left(30 \times 0.768 \right)$$

$$= 39.0 \, \text{MPa}$$

Hence, we can describe the maximum shear stress as:

$$\left(\tau_\theta \right)_{max} = 39 \, \text{MPa at an angle } \theta_s = -20°$$

$$-\left(\tau_\theta \right)_{max} = -39 \, \text{MPa at an angle } \theta_s = 70°$$

EXERCISE 1.13

The state of stress within an element in a load-bearing I-beam is shown in Figure 1.53. Determine the magnitude and orientation of the principal stresses and of the maximum shear stress.

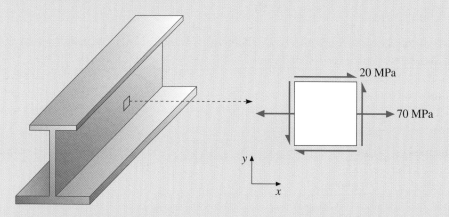

Figure 1.53   I-beam stress element

SAQ 1.7 (Learning outcomes 1.3 and 1.4)

Opening or closing a laptop computer (or clamshell mobile phone) can cause a combination of twisting and pulling that imposes a complex stress state in the plastic casing, particularly around the hinge. In normal use, such stresses are small and do not do any harm. However, accidentally dropping the computer, or bending the screen back too far, can generate stresses large enough to cause damage. Figure 1.54 shows the partial stress state at a point on the surface of a laptop computer casing at the moment that the screen was forced sharply back, resulting in a cracked hinge at that point. Estimate the unknown shear stress on the given element if the hinge material is known to break when a tensile stress of 50 MPa occurs in any direction.

Hint: assume that the maximum principal stress at failure is 50 MPa and use Equation (1.9) to determine the unknown shear stress.

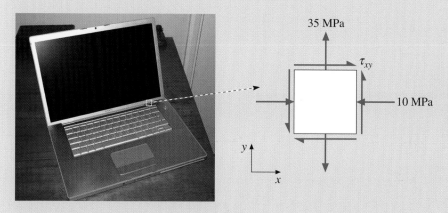

Figure 1.54   Stress state on a laptop hinge

7 MOHR'S CIRCLE

You may be quite happy to use and apply the plane stress transformation equations as a mathematical tool for unravelling the stress at a point. However, it is also important that you understand the relationships between the various types of stress we have been looking at and how they are influenced by orientation and applied stress state. To help, there is a graphical technique for representing the state of stress at a point that is exactly equivalent to using Equations (1.7) and (1.8). The technique provides an alternative means of determining stresses in various directions. Although less accurate, it was practically the *only* quick way of analysing stresses before the advent of the modern computer. More important for our purposes, it provides a convenient method of visualizing, for example, the connection between the principal stresses and the maximum shear stress.

The method is based on plotting σ_θ versus τ_θ, as you did for the special case of uniaxial stress in Exercise 1.8. If this is done for values of θ up to 180° then a *full circle* is obtained, as shown in Figure 1.55 for the stress state we examined in Figure 1.51. Note that positive values of σ_θ are drawn to the right of the origin in Figure 1.55 as expected, but that positive values of τ_θ are drawn *below* the origin. This is to comply with our convention for measuring the angle of rotation in an *anticlockwise* direction. For example, the stress state I have plotted at point X is that for which $\theta = 0°$, i.e. for a plane parallel to the x-face of the element in Figure 1.55. Point X' corresponds to $\theta = 30°$ and point Y to $\theta = 90°$; the latter represents a plane parallel to the element y-face. Hence, an increase in θ corresponds to an anticlockwise rotation around the circle. However, be careful to note that the angle of rotation appears *twice as large* in the circular representation; this is a consequence of the trigonometric functions containing 2θ in the transformation Equations (1.7) and (1.8).

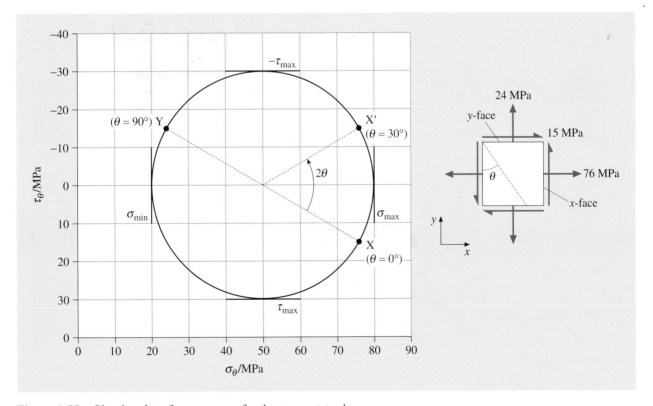

Figure 1.55   Circular plot of σ_θ versus τ_θ for the stress state shown

The same information can be extracted from the circle in Figure 1.55 as from the two sinusoidal curves drawn in Figure 1.51. The maximum and minimum values of the normal stress, i.e. the principal stresses $\sigma_1 = 80$ MPa and $\sigma_2 = 20$ MPa, occur where the circle intercepts the horizontal axis at $\tau_\theta = 0$, which is as we would expect given that the principal stress directions are along those axes where there is no shear stress acting. Since these points lie on a diameter of the circle they must represent stress states that are separated by a rotation of $90°$ (recall that the whole circle represents rotation through an angle of $180°$). Similarly, the maximum shear stress magnitude occurs at the upper and lower extremities of the circle, $\tau_{max} = 30$ MPa, again separated by a rotation of $90°$.

This type of plot is known as *Mohr's circle* after its originator Otto Mohr (Figure 1.56), a German engineer and educator who had a special interest in obtaining graphical solutions to problems. Mohr noticed that instead of plotting a large number of points, the stress circle of Figure 1.55 could be drawn very quickly if the end points of only one diameter, points X and Y for instance, were known. In fact, the values of σ_θ and τ_θ at $\theta = 0°$ and $\theta = 90°$ are easy to determine, as the following example illustrates.

Figure 1.56
Otto Mohr (1835–1918)

EXAMPLE

Use the stress transformation equations to find the coordinates on the diameter of Mohr's circle for which $\theta = 0°$ and $\theta = 90°$.

SOLUTION

When $\theta = 0°$, $\cos 2\theta = 1$ and $\sin 2\theta = 0$, so Equation (1.7) gives:

$$\sigma_\theta = \frac{1}{2}(\sigma_x + \sigma_y) + \frac{1}{2}(\sigma_x - \sigma_y)\cos 2\theta + \tau_{xy}\sin 2\theta$$

$$= \frac{1}{2}(\sigma_x + \sigma_y) + \frac{1}{2}(\sigma_x - \sigma_y)$$

$$= \sigma_x$$

[handwritten annotation:
$$\frac{\sigma_x + \sigma_y}{2} + \frac{\sigma_x - \sigma_y}{2}$$
$$= \frac{2\sigma_x}{2}$$
$$= \sigma_x$$
]

and Equation (1.8) gives:

$$\tau_\theta = -\frac{1}{2}(\sigma_x - \sigma_y)\sin 2\theta + \tau_{xy}\cos 2\theta$$

$$= \tau_{xy}$$

Hence, the first coordinate is (σ_x, τ_{xy}).

When $\theta = 90°$, $\cos 2\theta = -1$ and $\sin 2\theta = 0$, so Equation (1.7) gives:

$$\sigma_\theta = \sigma_y$$

and Equation (1.8) gives:

$$\tau_\theta = -\tau_{xy}$$

The other coordinate is $(\sigma_y, -\tau_{xy})$.

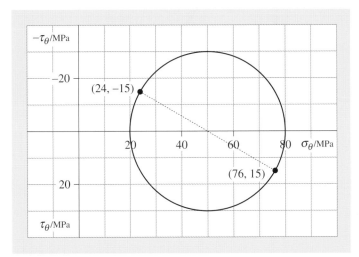

Figure 1.57   Mohr's circle construction for the stress state
$\sigma_x = 76$ MPa, $\sigma_y = 24$ MPa and $\tau_{xy} = 15$ MPa

By plotting these two points (σ_x, τ_{xy}) and $(\sigma_y, -\tau_{xy})$ on graph paper it is a simple matter to draw a diameter and then construct Mohr's circle using a pair of compasses. For the particular example used in Figure 1.55, we have:

$$\sigma_x = 76 \text{ MPa}$$

$$\sigma_y = 24 \text{ MPa}$$

$$\tau_{xy} = 15 \text{ MPa}.$$

So the extremities of the diameter are the points (76, 15) and (24, −15) and Mohr's circle can be drawn as shown in Figure 1.57. The centre of the circle lies at the point where the diameter intersects the horizontal axis, where $\tau_\theta = 0$ and $\sigma_\theta = \frac{1}{2}(\sigma_x + \sigma_y)$.

To summarize, the steps for plotting Mohr's stress circle are as follows:

1   Draw axes for σ_θ (horizontal axis) and τ_θ (vertical axis) with the same scale in both directions; σ_θ is positive to the *right* of the origin and τ_θ is positive *below* the origin.

2   Plot the points (σ_x, τ_{xy}) and $(\sigma_y, -\tau_{xy})$.

3   Join these points using a straight line; check that the line intercepts the horizontal axis at $\sigma_\theta = \frac{1}{2}(\sigma_x + \sigma_y)$.

4   Construct a circle with this line as a diameter and the intercept as the centre.

EXERCISE 1.14

Draw Mohr's circles for each of the eight stress states shown in Figure 1.58 (all stresses are in MPa).

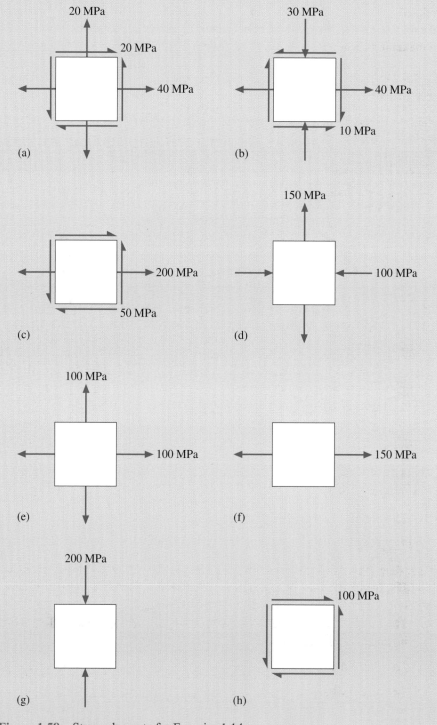

Figure 1.58   Stress elements for Exercise 1.14

7.1 Using Mohr's circle 1: extreme stresses

Once we have a known stress element and have drawn Mohr's circle, it is a simple matter to estimate the maximum and minimum stresses and the directions in which they act. This estimation is important, because the likelihood of failure in a material is related to the extremes of stress to which it is subjected. The following example and exercise demonstrate how to identify the magnitude and direction of the principal and maximum shear stresses acting at a point using Mohr's circle.

EXAMPLE

As a vehicle rides over rough ground its axle is subjected to combined torsion and bending. At one point on the surface of the shaft the stress state comprises an axial tensile stress of 30 MPa and a shear stress of 50 MPa, as shown in Figure 1.59. Using a Mohr's circle construction:

(a) estimate the principal stresses and sketch the inclined element on which they act

(b) estimate the maximum shear stresses and sketch the inclined element on which they act.

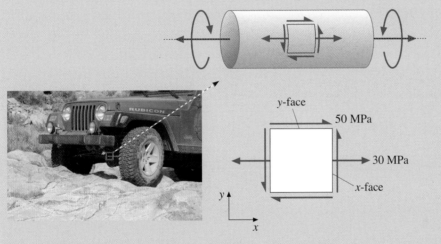

Figure 1.59 Stress state on the outer surface of a vehicle axle

SOLUTION

First draw Mohr's circle for the stress state $\sigma_x = 30$ MPa, $\sigma_y = 0$ MPa and $\tau_{xy} = 50$ MPa, using diameter end points for the element x-face at X = (30, 50) MPa and y-face at Y = (0, −50) MPa; see Figure 1.60(a).

(a) The principal stresses can be estimated from the points at which the circle intercepts the horizontal axis:

$\sigma_1 = 67$ MPa

$\sigma_2 = -37$ MPa.

The angle between the diameter XY and the horizontal axis, which represents the principal plane, is $2\theta \approx 74°$ anticlockwise. Hence, the principal stress element is inclined at an angle $\theta \approx 37°$ with respect to the initial element, as drawn in Figure 1.60(b).

(b) The maximum shear stresses occur at the upper and lower extremities of the circle: $\tau_{max} = 52$ MPa.

The angle between the diameter XY and the diameter defined by $\pm\tau_{max}$ is 16° clockwise. Hence, the element that experiences the maximum shear stress is inclined at an angle 8° clockwise with respect to the initial element, as drawn in Figure 1.60(c). Note that the normal stress associated with both $-\tau_{max}$ and $+\tau_{max}$ is the same, and is given by the value of σ_θ at the centre of the circle, which is 15 MPa in this case.

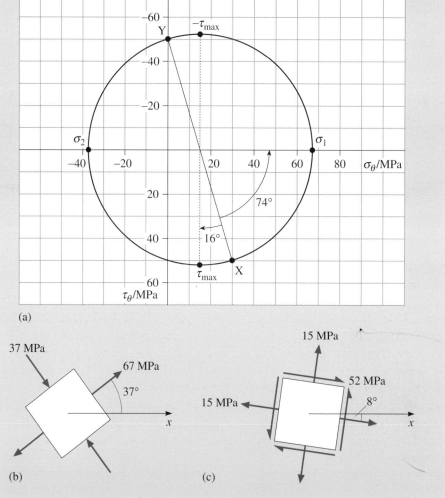

Figure 1.60 (a) Mohr's circle construction, (b) principal stress element and (c) maximum shear stress element for the shaft in Figure 1.59

EXERCISE 1.15

(a) A small piece of pressurized pipework is gripped by a wrench and subject to a torsion so that a point on its outer surface experiences the combined stress state shown in Figure 1.61. Use Mohr's circle to estimate the principal and maximum shear stresses, and draw elements representing the stress states in each of these two cases.

(b) Confirm your answers to part (a) by calculation, using the equations for the principal and maximum shear stress magnitudes and orientations, Equations (1.8)–(1.11).

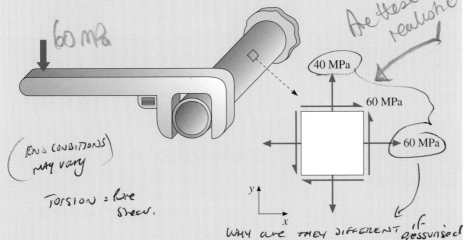

Figure 1.61   Stress state on the outer surface of some pressurized pipework

Now, you should be starting to appreciate that there are various ways of approaching stress analysis problems. Using equations is more accurate than drawing Mohr's circle, but the latter helps give a useful picture of what is happening, particularly with respect to the orientation of the stresses. In fact, there is a more accurate way of using Mohr's circle, which you may find useful if you need to know the limiting stresses and their orientations. It involves the use of basic trigonometry to calculate the radius of the circle, so that the principal and maximum shear stresses can be determined more accurately. I have outlined how this is done in ☑ **Analysing Mohr's circle** ☑. The idea is that as you become more familiar with the Mohr's circle construction, you can just sketch the appropriate circle for a particular element and use it as an aid to calculation. You can follow this approach, or stick to the purely graphical or computational methods. In the end it really is up to you which method, or combination of methods, you use.

☑ Analysing Mohr's circle

Obtaining principal and maximum shear stresses

An accurate analysis of Mohr's circle can be obtained by using simple trigonometry to determine the circle radius, from which the principal stresses and maximum shear stress can easily be deduced. In using this method it is not necessary to draw Mohr's circle exactly to scale on graph paper (although it always helps!); a simple sketch will suffice.

To demonstrate, let us look again at the stress state we examined in the last example concerning a vehicle axle: $\sigma_x = 30$ MPa, $\sigma_y = 0$ MPa and $\tau_{xy} = 50$ MPa. In Figure 1.62 I have sketched Mohr's circle using diameter end points for element face X at (30, 50) MPa and face Y at (0, −50) MPa, but this time I have also added the centre point C at ($\frac{1}{2}(\sigma_x + \sigma_y)$, 0). The diameter XCY can be used to construct two identical right-angled triangles (shaded in the figure), either of which can be used to calculate the radius of the circle using Pythagoras's theorem:

$$\text{radius } CX = CY = \sqrt{50^2 + 15^2} = 52.2 \text{ MPa}$$

Once the radius is known, the principal stresses and maximum shear stress are simple to deduce:

the maximum shear stress is equal to the radius of the circle

$$\tau_{max} = 52.2 \text{ MPa}$$

the maximum principal stress is given by the centre coordinate plus the radius

$$\sigma_1 = 15 \text{ MPa} + 52.2 \text{ MPa} = 67.2 \text{ MPa}$$

the minimum principal stress is given by the centre coordinate minus the radius

$$\sigma_2 = 15 \text{ MPa} − 52.2 \text{ MPa} = −37.2 \text{ MPa}$$

It is necessary to compute the orientation θ_p of the principal planes using Equation (1.10).

$$\tan 2\theta_p = \frac{2\tau_{xy}}{\sigma_x - \sigma_y} = \frac{(2 \times 50) \text{ MPa}}{(30 - 0) \text{ MPa}} = 3.33$$

$$2\theta_p = 73.3° \text{ or } 253.3°$$

$$\theta_p = 36.7° \text{ or } 126.7°$$

and from Figure 1.62 it is clear that the angle between the plane represented by X and the plane containing σ_1 is given by $2\theta_p = 73.3°$, $\theta_p = 36.7°$.

The maximum shear stress plane is 45° anticlockwise from the maximum principal stress plane (90° anticlockwise in Figure 1.62), i.e. the maximum shear stress plane is 45° − 36.7° = 8.3° anticlockwise from the known stress plane X.

Note that this approach works only for principal stresses and maximum shear stresses. If you need to know the stresses in any other directions you must construct Mohr's circle accurately, or use the equations.

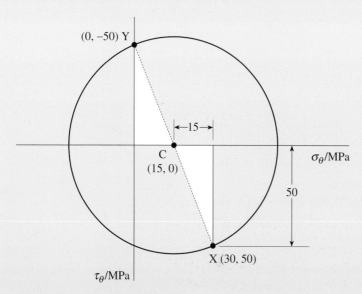

Figure 1.62   Mohr's circle sketch

7.2 Using Mohr's circle 2: stresses in other directions

As well as estimating principal stresses and maximum shear stresses, the Mohr's circle model also enables us to determine stresses in any other direction at the same point. Look at how this is done by following the next example, and then have a go for yourself.

EXAMPLE

The stress at a point on the surface of the 'down tube' of a bicycle frame while it is being ridden over rough ground is shown in Figure 1.63. Note that the given element is aligned with the 'top tube' of the frame. Use Mohr's circle to estimate the shear and normal stresses that act on a plane at right angles to the axis of the down tube at this point (i.e. on the dotted 45° section sketched across the stress element).

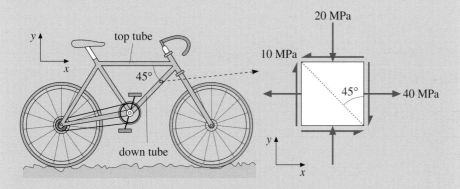

Figure 1.63   Stress elements on a bicycle frame down tube

SOLUTION

To determine the (non-principal) stresses in an arbitrary direction using Mohr's circle, it is necessary to make an accurate construction of the circle using graph paper. The Mohr's circle for the element of Figure 1.63, plotted using the diameter XY, is shown in Figure 1.64(a).

The coordinates at X are (40, −10) MPa, corresponding to stresses (σ_x, τ_{xy}).

The coordinates at Y are (−20, 10) MPa, corresponding to stresses (σ_y, −τ_{xy}).

To find the stresses at $\theta = 45°$ it is necessary to draw a diameter, X′Y′, that has been rotated anticlockwise through twice this angle, $2\theta = 90°$, as shown. This is the same as considering the stresses on a new element with its faces parallel to axes x′and y′ that are inclined at 45° to the original axes.

Reading from the graph:

The coordinates at X′ are (0, −30) MPa, corresponding to the *transformed* stresses ($\sigma_{x'}$, $\tau_{x'y'}$).

The coordinates at Y′ are (20, 30) MPa, corresponding to the *transformed* stresses ($\sigma_{y'}$, $-\tau_{x'y'}$).

Hence, the stresses on the inclined element are:

$\sigma_{x'} = 0$ MPa

$\sigma_{y'} = 20$ MPa

$\tau_{x'y'} = -30$ MPa.

as sketched in Figure 1.64(b).

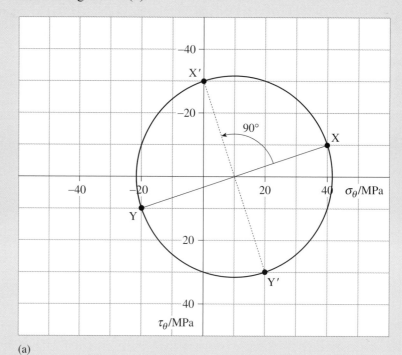

(a)

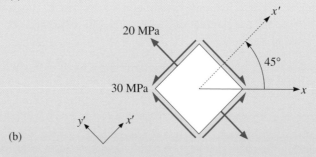

(b)

Figure 1.64   (a) Mohr's circle for the stress element in Figure 1.63; (b) stresses on an element inclined at an angle of 45° to the *x*-direction

SAQ 1.8 (Learning outcomes 1.4, 1.5 and 1.7)

Figure 1.65 again shows the bicycle frame of the last example, but this time the stress is given at a point on the 'seat tube' of the frame.

(a) Use Mohr's circle to calculate the shear and normal stresses on a plane at right angles to the axis of the seat tube, equivalent to rotating the x-face of the element clockwise through $55°$.

Software that automates the construction of Mohr's circle can be found on the course DVD. ↵

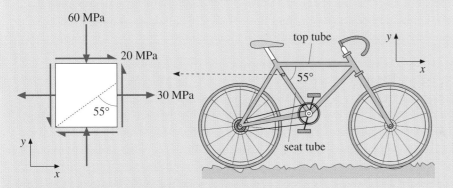

Figure 1.65   Stress element on a bicycle frame

(b) Confirm your answer to part (a) by calculation, using the plane stress transformation equations.

8 THE STRESS TENSOR: DESCRIBING STRESS IN THREE DIMENSIONS

Up until now we have assumed a state of two-dimensional stress, for which stresses in the plane of the x- and y-coordinate axes only are considered. In a lot of useful cases, such a two-dimensional simplification is an adequate approximation for the purposes of engineering analysis. However, before moving on it is important to remind you that stresses in the third dimension can and do exist, and under certain circumstances we will need to take them into account.

We can extend our two-dimensional description of plane stress (see Section 5.1) to three dimensions by considering an infinitesimally small *cubic* element of material with its faces aligned parallel to the axes of our chosen xyz-coordinate system, as shown in Figure 1.66. Under general loading, each cube face will experience one independent normal stress component (e.g. σ_z on the z-face) and two independent shear stress components (e.g. τ_{zx} and τ_{zy} on the z-face), i.e. nine stress components in total. Recall that, using our chosen notation, the first shear stress suffix indicates the plane in which the shear stress acts and the second subscript refers to the shear stress direction. Hence, shear stress τ_{zx} acts on the plane perpendicular to the z-direction (the z-face of the cube) and is parallel to the x-axis.

For convenience, the nine stress components that completely define the three-dimensional stress at a particular point in a stressed member are sometimes arranged into an array:

$$\begin{bmatrix} \sigma_x & \tau_{xy} & \tau_{xz} \\ \tau_{yx} & \sigma_y & \tau_{yz} \\ \tau_{zx} & \tau_{zy} & \sigma_z \end{bmatrix}$$

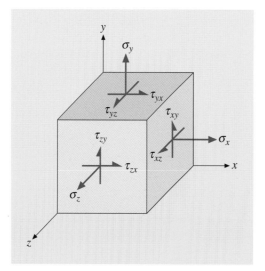

Figure 1.66   Stress components acting on a three-dimensional element

Such a grouping of components is called a *tensor* in mathematics, in this case a stress tensor. Of course, as noted previously for a two-dimensional plane stress element, opposing shear stresses must be equal to avoid rotation of the element; hence $\tau_{xy} = \tau_{yx}$, $\tau_{yz} = \tau_{zy}$ and $\tau_{zx} = \tau_{xz}$. In the three-dimensional stress tensor, therefore, for equilibrium there are only six unknown components, as three of the six shear stresses are complementary to the other three.

For plane stress analysis, all the components of stress in the z-direction are zero and the stress tensor becomes:

$$\begin{bmatrix} \sigma_x & \tau_{xy} & 0 \\ \tau_{yx} & \sigma_y & 0 \\ 0 & 0 & 0 \end{bmatrix}$$

which is usually written more concisely as:

$$\begin{bmatrix} \sigma_x & \tau_{xy} \\ \tau_{yx} & \sigma_y \end{bmatrix}$$

Arranging stress components in a tensor is a useful shorthand way of summarizing the stress at a point, and also an important mathematical tool: stresses are stored and manipulated in tensor form during finite element calculations, for example. I do not want to do any complicated three-dimensional analysis at this stage, but you can get a feel for how a tensor can be used to present data, as well as revising all you've learnt so far, by studying a two-dimensional problem in ☑ **The distribution of stress in a simple hook design** ☑.

So, under what circumstances is it necessary to carry out a full three-dimensional analysis, rather than a two-dimensional one? Well, three-dimensional analyses tend to be very complex mathematically, and as an engineer it often depends on how much time, money and effort you have to throw at the problem. You have seen that plane stress is fine for analysing the loading of certain geometries where the stress in one direction can be ignored, and it is also useful for determining the stress at the surface of more complex structures, such as aircraft wings and bicycle frames. However, to determine the stresses *inside* an aircraft wing or across the intricate geometry of a turbine blade it is necessary to model the structure in three dimensions, often using the finite element method. On the other hand, some smaller, relatively simple components also require analysis in three dimensions, often because their geometry just can't be captured in two dimensions alone. As it turns out, one example is a crane hook which, if correctly designed, does not have a uniform thickness or shape whichever way you look at it. You will have gained some insight into why this is the case by attempting SAQ 1.9.

☑ The distribution of stress in a simple hook design

In this part you have looked in some detail at how to describe and calculate the state of stress at any point in a material. Let us start to apply some of this knowledge to the analysis of a simple, load-bearing engineering component, namely a hook. Like the tie bar that we looked at in Section 2, a hook is used to support tensile loads, but it has a non-uniform, curved geometry that means a large part of it is subject to 'complex' (i.e. non-uniaxial) stresses even when it is loaded in one direction only. What I would like to do is try out a crude design for a hook and examine the likely stress distribution using the finite element method. Later in this course we will address other methods of analysing the stress in a component of this type, and explore ways in which the simple design can be improved.

Now, I know that hooks often come in rather odd shapes, but for the time being I will assume a simple geometry of approximately equal width (~10 mm) all round, with a circular hook for attaching the load, and a circular eyehole for fixing to a crane or hoist; see Figure 1.67. The two-dimensional finite element analysis I will use assumes plane stress ($\sigma_z = 0$), so I am in effect attempting to simulate the stress state in a thin plate of material. Again, this isn't very realistic, but it should nevertheless give me an idea of where the highest stresses might occur, if not their precise magnitude. Because this is a two-dimensional analysis the component does not really have any thickness in the z-direction. However, for the purpose of calculating stresses the finite element code assumes an arbitrary thickness of 1 mm. As with the tie bar, I will apply the load via two circular pins, set to apply a constant tensile force of 500 N parallel to the y-axis.

The imposition of a load, a movement or any other constraint on a finite element mesh is known as a *boundary condition*.

The 500 N applied load would create an axial stress of 50 MPa in a uniform strip of material 10 mm wide by 1 mm thick; this is the expected tensile stress in the neck of the hook.

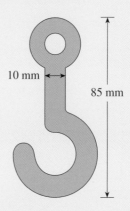

Figure 1.67   Sketch of the hook geometry

The actual stress state predicted by my finite element analysis of the loaded hook geometry is shown in Figure 1.68.

The finite element solution involves calculation of all three independent plane stress components σ_x, σ_y and τ_{xy}. However, since it is difficult to look at these all at once, Figure 1.68 shows a contour map for only one of these stress components, σ_y, parallel to the direction of loading. Take a careful look at the stress distribution, making use of the colour key provided. As with the tie bar, there are considerable localized contact stresses associated with the way the loading is applied by the circular pins. Because I want to concentrate on the hook geometry itself, I will ask you to ignore these anomalies and turn your attention to the stress distribution elsewhere. In particular, you may be quite surprised by the stresses that are generated along section CD. To help you with interpretation of the finite element results, go through the following SAQ.

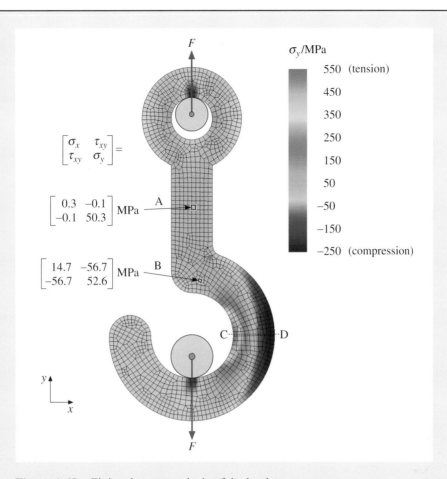

Figure 1.68 Finite element analysis of the hook geometry

SAQ 1.9 (Learning outcomes 1.5, 1.6 and 1.8)

Refer to the finite element results for the hook mesh presented in Figure 1.68. The average stress tensor within individual finite elements is shown at points A and B.

(a) Comment on the state of stress at A. What are the approximate magnitudes and orientations of the principal stresses at A?

(b) Comment on the state of stress at B. Determine the magnitudes and orientations of the principal stresses at B.

(c) Sketch a graph of the approximate variation in σ_y along line CD.

   Hint: consider where σ_y is zero, and where it attains a maximum and a minimum value.

(d) What do you think may have caused the stress distribution along line CD?

(e) Can you think of any design modifications that would help reduce the high stresses along CD?

Figure 1.69 Principal stresses in three dimensions

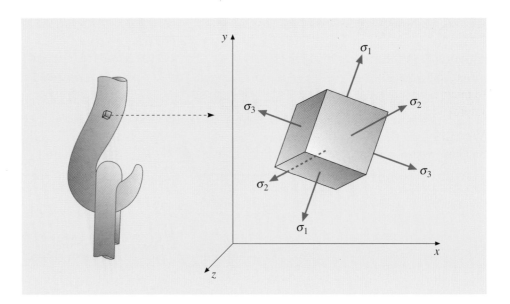

To help you appreciate the difficulties associated with analysing such an asymmetric component, it is worth pointing out that *three* principal stresses on three mutually perpendicular principal planes need to be determined (Figure 1.69). These principal stresses, conventionally denoted by σ_1, σ_2 and σ_3 (where $\sigma_1 \geq \sigma_2 \geq \sigma_3$), cannot be deduced by two-dimensional analysis alone. Undaunted, we will be revisiting the crane hook again during this course.

9 SUMMARY

This first part of the course has introduced you to the concept of stress which will run throughout your study of T357. Loads on components, products and structures lead to internal stresses, and it is stresses which can lead to failure if a product has been improperly designed or if it is exposed to unexpectedly high loading in use.

We will move on in Part 2 to look at the strains which arise from internal stresses, and how measurements of strain can be used to directly calculate stresses.

LEARNING OUTCOMES

After you have studied Block 1 Part 1 you should be able to do the following.

1.1 Describe the relationship between external loading and internal stress distribution within engineering components.

1.2 Describe and quantify normal and shear stresses in engineering components and structures.

1.3 Be able to represent and interpret stress elements describing the two-dimensional state of stress at a point.

1.4 Use plane stress transformation equations, or Mohr's circle, to determine stresses on a section of known orientation for a given stress state in a material body.

1.5 Determine principal stresses and their orientations for a given state of plane stress using formulae or Mohr's circle.

1.6 Recognize and interpret the stress output from simple finite element analyses.

1.7 Understand the application of a two-dimensional plane stress approximation to the analysis of stress in engineering components.

1.8 Understand the application of two-dimensional and three-dimensional interpretations of stress state, and recognize and apply the notation of stress components using tensors.

ANSWERS TO EXERCISES

EXERCISE 1.1

(a) At section P:

$$\sigma = \frac{F}{A} = \frac{F}{\pi r^2} = \frac{800 \text{ N}}{\pi \times \left(8 \times 10^{-3}\right)^2 \text{ m}^2} = 3.98 \text{ MPa}$$

At section Q:

$$\sigma = \frac{F}{A} = \frac{F}{\pi r^2} = \frac{800 \text{ N}}{\pi \times \left(5 \times 10^{-3}\right)^2 \text{ m}^2} = 10.2 \text{ MPa}$$

These stresses are a quarter of those calculated in the example. (Stress is proportional to the square of the radius, so doubling the radius decreases the stress fourfold.)

(b) From the definition of stress, $\sigma = F/A$, it is necessary to halve the area in order to double the stress, for the same applied load.

(Area can be written as $A = \pi r^2 = \pi \left(\dfrac{d}{2}\right)^2 = \dfrac{\pi}{4} d^2$, where d is the diameter.)

At section P, half the area in the original example is 2.51×10^{-5} m²; hence, the new diameter is:

$$d = \sqrt{\frac{4A}{\pi}} = \sqrt{\frac{4 \times (2.51 \times 10^{-5}) \text{ m}^2}{\pi}} = 5.65 \times 10^{-3} \text{m} = 5.65 \text{ mm}$$

At section Q, the new area is 9.82×10^{-6} m²; hence, the new diameter is:

$$d = \sqrt{\frac{4A}{\pi}} = \sqrt{\frac{4 \times (9.82 \times 10^{-6}) \text{ m}^2}{\pi}} = 3.54 \times 10^{-3} \text{m} = 3.54 \text{ mm}$$

EXERCISE 1.2

The cross-sectional area can be found by considering it to consist of three rectangles, two of which have dimensions 120 mm × 10 mm and one of which has dimensions 60 mm × 10 mm. Thus:

$$A = 2\left(120 \times 10^{-3} \times 10 \times 10^{-3}\right) \text{m}^2 + \left(60 \times 10^{-3} \times 10 \times 10^{-3}\right) \text{m}^2$$
$$= 3 \times 10^{-3} \text{ m}^2$$

The maximum compressive force is:

$$F = \sigma A = -250 \times 10^6 \text{ N m}^{-2} \times 3 \times 10^{-3} \text{ m}^{-2}$$
$$= -7.50 \times 10^5 \text{ N}$$

EXERCISE 1.3

(a) The force corresponding to a stress of 0.5 MPa in a single lap joint of area 25×25 mm^2 is:

$$F = \tau\, A = 0.5 \times 10^6\, \text{N m}^{-2} \times \left(25 \times 10^{-3}\right)^2 \text{m}^2 = 312.5\ \text{N}$$

and is the maximum tensile load that the glue can bear.

For the double lap joint, the tensile load that can be supported at a single interface is the same as for the single lap joint of the same dimensions calculated above (i.e. 312.5 N).

This is half the total load-bearing capacity of the joint ($F/2$, see Figure 1.70), and is borne by each of the right-hand members. The total load, 625 N, is carried in the left-hand member.

(b) Using $F = \sigma A$:

$$A = 25 \times 10^{-3}\ \text{m} \times 1 \times 10^{-3}\ \text{m} = 25 \times 10^{-6}\ \text{m}^2$$

At failure $\sigma = 80$ MPa, so the force at failure is:

$$F = 80 \times 10^6\ \text{N m}^{-2} \times 25 \times 10^{-6}\ \text{m}^{-2} = 2000\ \text{N}$$

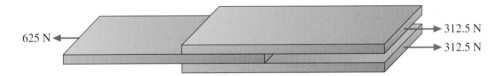

625 N

312.5 N

312.5 N

Figure 1.70   Forces on double lap joint shown in Figure 1.15(b)

EXERCISE 1.4

This joint is in single shear, so the shear force carried by the total bolt cross-sectional area has the same magnitude as the external applied tensile force (i.e. 20 kN).

Each of the two bolts, radius r, must carry 10 kN, and for a maximum allowable stress of 100 MPa we have, in a single bolt:

$$\tau = \frac{F}{\pi r^2}$$

$$r^2 = \frac{F}{\pi \tau}$$

$$r = \sqrt{\frac{F}{\pi \tau}} = \sqrt{\frac{10 \times 10^3\ \text{N}}{\pi \times 100 \times 10^6\ \text{N m}^{-2}}} = 5.64 \times 10^{-3}\ \text{m}$$

So the required minimum bolt diameter is 11.3 mm.

EXERCISE 1.5

(a) First find length PQ:

$$\cos 30° = \frac{40\ \text{mm}}{\text{PQ}}, \text{ hence PQ} = \frac{40\ \text{mm}}{\cos 30°} = 46.2\ \text{mm}$$

Section area $A = 46.2 \times 10^{-3}\ \text{m} \times 20 \times 10^{-3}\ \text{m} = 924 \times 10^{-6}\ \text{m}^2$

(b) $F = 200$ kN, for force equilibrium.

(c) Normal force: $F_n = F \cos 30° = 200$ kN $\times \cos 30° = 173.2$ kN.

(d) Shear force: $F_s = F \sin 30° = 200$ kN $\times \sin 30° = 100$ kN.

(e) Normal stress:

$$\sigma = \frac{F_n}{A} = \frac{173.2 \times 10^3 \text{ N}}{924 \times 10^{-6} \text{ m}^2} = 187 \text{ MPa}$$

Shear stress:

$$\tau = \frac{F_s}{A} = \frac{100 \times 10^3 \text{ N}}{924 \times 10^{-6} \text{ m}^2} = 108 \text{ MPa}$$

EXERCISE 1.6

Table 1.2   Stresses on inclined sections for Exercise 1.6

Angle of section, θ	0°	15°	30°	45°	60°	75°	90°
σ_θ/MPa	20.0	18.7	15.0	10.0	5.0	1.3	0
τ_θ/MPa	0	5.0	8.7	10.0	8.7	5.0	0

EXERCISE 1.7

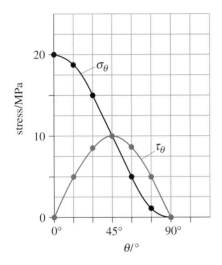

Figure 1.71   Plot of stress versus angle of section θ

(a) $\theta = 0°$

(b) $\theta = 45°$

(c) $\theta = 0°$ and $\theta = 90°$

EXERCISE 1.8

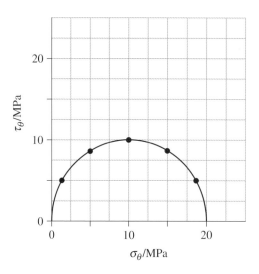

Figure 1.72   Plot of τ_θ versus θ

The curve should approximate to a semicircle.

EXERCISE 1.9

I can think of a few household items, such as corkscrews, where there are both twisting and pulling forces used. Likewise, if I am not careful when using screwdrivers I might be twisting and bending the shaft at the same time.

Car axles will have the weight of the car acting on them, plus lateral forces from the wheels during cornering.

EXERCISE 1.10

$\sigma_x = 50$ MPa, $\sigma_y = 100$ MPa and $\tau_{xy} = 75$ MPa.

EXERCISE 1.11

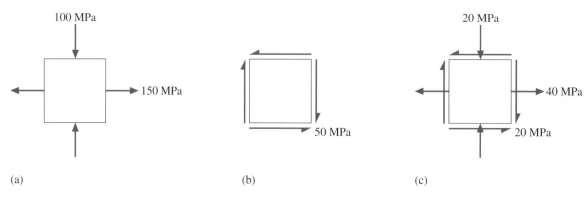

Figure 1.73   Stress element solutions

EXERCISE 1.12

The stresses on the rotated element are fully characterized if we calculate the normal stresses on perpendicular planes with $\theta = -40°$ and $\theta = -40 + 90 = 50°$, along with a single shear stress.

For the given element $\sigma_x = -100$ MPa, $\sigma_y = 0$ MPa and $\tau_{xy} = -50$ MPa; hence, using Equations (1.7) and (1.8) for $\theta = -40°$:

$$\left(\sigma_\theta\right)_{-40} = \frac{1}{2}(-100 + 0) + \frac{1}{2}(-100 - 0)\cos(-80°) - 50\sin(-80°)$$
$$= -50 - 8.68 + 49.24$$
$$= -9.4 \text{ MPa}$$

$$\left(\tau_\theta\right)_{-40} = -\frac{1}{2}(-100 - 0)\sin(-80°) - 50\cos(-80°)$$
$$= -49.24 - 8.68$$
$$= -57.9 \text{ MPa}$$

and for $\theta = 50°$

$$\left(\sigma_\theta\right)_{50} = \frac{1}{2}(-100 + 0) + \frac{1}{2}(-100 - 0)\cos100° - 50\sin100°$$
$$= -50 + 8.68 - 49.24$$
$$= -90.6 \text{ MPa}$$

The rotated element is shown in Figure 1.74.

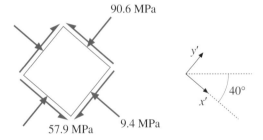

90.6 MPa

57.9 MPa   9.4 MPa

Figure 1.74   Stress element from Figure 1.49 rotated by 40° clockwise

EXERCISE 1.13

The element stresses are $\sigma_x = 70$ MPa, $\sigma_y = 0$ MPa and $\tau_{xy} = 20$ MPa.

The principal stresses are:

$$\sigma_{1,2} = \frac{\sigma_x + \sigma_y}{2} \pm \sqrt{\left(\frac{\sigma_x - \sigma_y}{2}\right)^2 + \tau_{xy}^2} = \frac{70 + 0}{2} \pm \sqrt{\left(\frac{70 - 0}{2}\right)^2 + 20^2}$$
$$= 35 \pm 40.3 \text{ MPa}$$

That is, $\sigma_1 = 75.3$ MPa and $\sigma_2 = -5.3$ MPa.

The principal stress orientations are given by:

$$\tan 2\theta_p = \frac{2\tau_{xy}}{\sigma_x - \sigma_y} = \frac{(2 \times 20)\,\text{MPa}}{(70 - 0)\,\text{MPa}} = \frac{4}{7}$$

$$2\theta_p = 29.7°, \ 209.7°$$

$$\theta_p = 14.9°, \ 104.9°$$

Substituting $2\theta_p = 29.7°$ into Equation (1.7):

$$(\sigma_\theta)_{14.9} = \frac{1}{2}(70 + 0) + \frac{1}{2}(70 - 0)\cos 29.7° + 20\sin 29.7°$$

$$= 75.3\,\text{MPa}$$

So, the major principal stress $\sigma_1 = 75$ MPa at $\theta_p = 15°$.

The minor principal stress $\sigma_2 = -5$ MPa at $\theta_p = 105°$.

The maximum shear stress:

$$(\tau_\theta)_{\text{max}} = \pm\sqrt{\left(\frac{\sigma_x - \sigma_y}{2}\right)^2 + \tau_{xy}^2} = \pm\sqrt{\left(\frac{70 - 0}{2}\right)^2 + 20^2}$$

$$= \pm 40.3\,\text{MPa}$$

The maximum shear stress orientations are:

$$\tan 2\theta_s = -\frac{\sigma_x - \sigma_y}{2\tau_{xy}} = -\frac{(70 - 0)\ \text{MPa}}{(2 \times 20)\ \text{MPa}} = -\frac{7}{4}$$

$$2\theta_s = -60.2°, \ 119.8°$$

$$\theta_s = -30.1°, \ 59.9°$$

Using Equation (1.7):

$$(\tau_\theta)_{-30.1} = -\frac{1}{2}(70 - 0)\sin(-60.25°) + 20\cos(-60.25°)$$

$$= 40.3\,\text{MPa}$$

So, the maximum shear stress is:

$$(\tau_\theta)_{\text{max}} = 40\,\text{MPa at } \theta_s = -30°$$

$$-(\tau_\theta)_{\text{max}} = -40\,\text{MPa at } \theta_s = 60°$$

EXERCISE 1.14

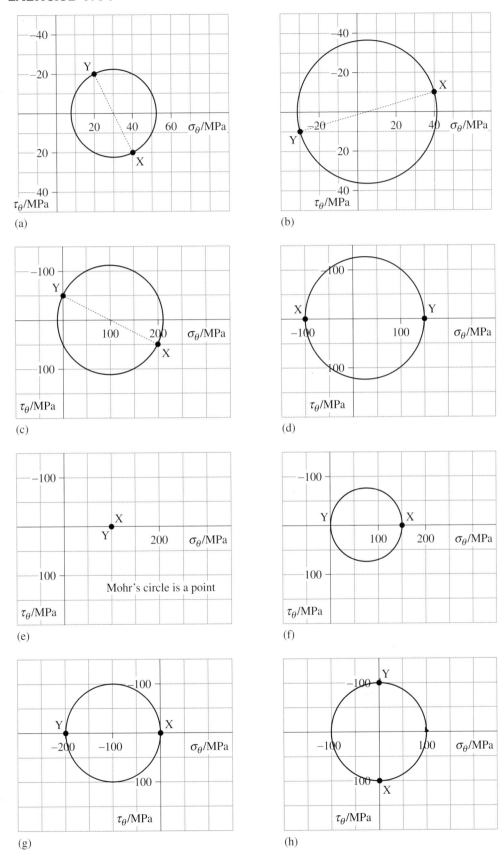

Figure 1.75 Mohr's circle solutions for stress elements in Figure 1.58

EXERCISE 1.15

(a) The element stresses are $\sigma_x = 60$ MPa, $\sigma_y = 40$ MPa and $\tau_{xy} = 60$ MPa. Your Mohr's circle, principal stress element and maximum shear stress element should look something like those in Figure 1.76.

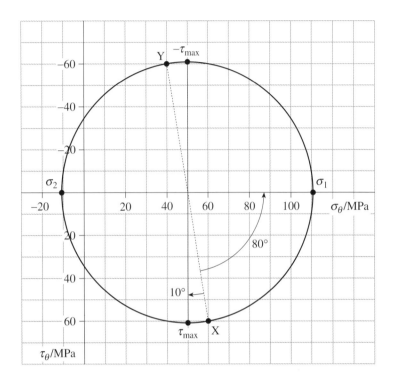

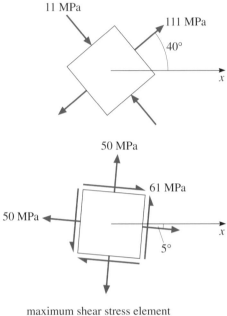

principal stress element

maximum shear stress element

Figure 1.76 Mohr's circle and stress elements for Figure 1.61

(b) Principal stresses by calculation:

$$\sigma_{1,2} = \frac{\sigma_x + \sigma_y}{2} \pm \sqrt{\left(\frac{\sigma_x - \sigma_y}{2}\right)^2 + \tau_{xy}^2} = \frac{60 + 40}{2} \pm \sqrt{\left(\frac{60 - 40}{2}\right)^2 + 60^2}$$

$$= 50 \pm 60.8 \text{ MPa}$$

That is, $\sigma_1 = 110.8$ MPa and $\sigma_2 = -10.8$ MPa.

$$\tan 2\theta_p = \frac{2\tau_{xy}}{\sigma_x - \sigma_y} = \frac{(2 \times 60)\,\text{MPa}}{(60 - 40)\,\text{MPa}} = 6$$

$$\theta_p = 40.3°, \ 130.3°$$

Maximum shear stress:

$$(\tau_\theta)_{max} = \pm\sqrt{\left(\frac{\sigma_x - \sigma_y}{2}\right)^2 + \tau_{xy}^2} = \pm\sqrt{\left(\frac{60 - 40}{2}\right)^2 + 60^2}$$

$$= \pm 60.8 \text{ MPa}$$

$$\tan 2\theta_s = -\frac{\sigma_x - \sigma_y}{2\tau_{xy}} = -\frac{(60 - 40)\,\text{MPa}}{(2 \times 60)\,\text{MPa}} = -\frac{1}{6}$$

$$\theta_s = -4.7°, \ 85.4°$$

ANSWERS TO SELF-ASSESSMENT QUESTIONS

SAQ 1.1

(a) Cross-sectional area of the material in the column:

$$A = (\text{external dimension})^2 - (\text{internal dimension})^2$$

$$A = \left(50 \times 10^{-3}\right)^2 m^2 - \left(38 \times 10^{-3}\right)^2 m^2$$

$$= 1.06 \times 10^{-3} \ m^2$$

Stress in the column material:

$$\sigma = \frac{F}{A} = \frac{-350 \times 10^3 \ N}{1.06 \times 10^{-3} \ m^2} = -330 \ MPa$$

The average compressive stress in the column is 330 MPa.

(b) Minimum area required to support a stress of 220 MPa for the same load is:

$$A = \frac{F}{\sigma} = \frac{-350 \times 10^3 \ N}{-220 \times 10^6 \ N \, m^{-2}} = 1.59 \times 10^{-3} \ m^2$$

The new cross-sectional area must be at least $1.59 \times 10^{-3} \ m^2$ and the external dimension of the square section remains the same:

$$A = (\text{external dimension})^2 - (\text{internal dimension})^2$$

$$\text{internal dimension} = \sqrt{\left(50 \times 10^{-3}\right)^2 m^2 - 1.59 \times 10^{-3} \ m^2}$$

$$= 30.2 \times 10^{-3} \ m$$

$$= 30.2 \ mm$$

Hence the wall thickness needs to be $(50 - 30.2)/2 = 9.9$ mm

SAQ 1.2

(a) For each joint member to be in equilibrium the shear force across every surface must be 2 kN (see Figure 1.77). The overlap of the splice on each plank is 20 mm. The corresponding surface shear stress on each overlap area of 20 mm × 50 mm is:

$$\tau = \frac{F}{A} = \frac{2000 \ N}{\left(20 \times 10^{-3}\right) m \times \left(50 \times 10^{-3}\right) m} = 2 \times 10^6 \ N \, m^{-2} = 2 \ MPa$$

(b) To halve the shear stress to 1 MPa it is necessary to double the surface area over which the shear stress acts. For the same width of member, this is achieved by doubling the overlap length from 20 mm to 40 mm. The required length of splice is then 40 mm + 10 mm + 40 mm = 90 mm.

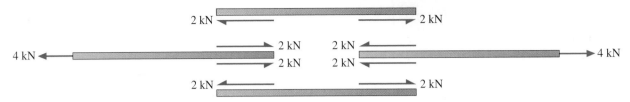

Figure 1.77   Balance of forces across the spliced joint in Figure 1.16

SAQ 1.3

The pin experiences shear forces of magnitude $F/2$ across two cross sections (Figure 1.78):

$$\text{shear force} = \frac{F}{2}$$

The cross-sectional area is given by:

$$A = \pi \times \left(\frac{25}{2} \times 10^{-3} \right)^2 \text{ m}^2 = 490.9 \times 10^{-6} \text{ m}^2$$

and is related to the shear stress by:

$$\text{shear stress, } \tau = \frac{\text{shear force}}{A}$$

or

$$\text{shear force} = \tau \times A$$

Thus:

$$\frac{F}{2} = 100 \times 10^6 \text{ N m}^{-2} \times 490.9 \times 10^{-6} \text{ m}^2 = 49.1 \text{ kN}$$

$$F = 2 \times 49.1 \text{ kN} = 98.2 \text{ kN}$$

The maximum allowable pull is 98 kN.

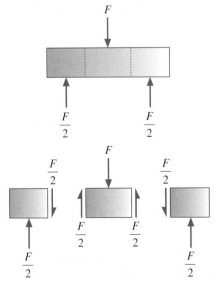

Figure 1.78   Forces in eye bar in Figure 1.23

SAQ 1.4

The cylindrical 'plug' of material that is punched out experiences shear forces of magnitude F, equal to the punch force, that act over the sheared surface area of the plug.

The curved surface area of the plug over which the shearing force acts is shown in Figure 1.79.

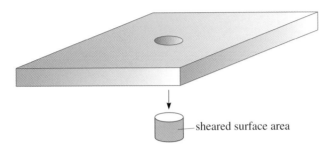

Figure 1.79 Punching a hole in a plate

The sheared surface area is:

$$A = \text{circumference} \times \text{height}$$
$$= \pi \left(25 \times 10^{-3} \right) \text{m} \times \left(10 \times 10^{-3} \right) \text{m}$$
$$= 785.4 \times 10^{-6} \text{ m}^2$$

The shear force is:

$$F = \tau A = 300 \times 10^6 \text{ N m}^{-2} \times 785.4 \times 10^{-6} \text{ m}^2 = 236 \text{ kN}$$

The required force is 236 kN.

SAQ 1.5

(a) The shearing in the head, height 10 mm, acts over a diameter d of 10 mm. Hence, the area over which the force acts is:

$$A = \pi d \times \text{height}$$
$$= \pi \left(10 \times 10^{-3} \right) \text{m} \times \left(10 \times 10^{-3} \right) \text{m}$$
$$= 314.2 \times 10^{-6} \text{ m}^2$$

The applied force of 25 kN is distributed over the whole of this area, giving shear stress:

$$\tau = \frac{F}{A} = \frac{25 \times 10^3 \text{ N}}{314.2 \times 10^{-6} \text{ m}^2} = 79.6 \text{ MPa}$$

(b) Similarly, the shearing in the plate, thickness 6 mm, acts over a diameter d of 30 mm:

$$\tau = \frac{F}{A} = \frac{F}{\pi d \times \text{thickness}} = \frac{25 \times 10^3 \text{ N}}{\pi \left(30 \times 10^{-3} \right) \text{m} \times \left(6 \times 10^{-3} \right) \text{m}} = 44.2 \text{ MPa}$$

SAQ 1.6

Rotating the given x-axis anticlockwise through 30° will bring it to point at right angles to the direction of the grain. Hence, transformation Equations (1.7) and (1.8) can be used with $\theta = 30°$, $\sigma_x = 6$ MPa, $\sigma_y = -14$ MPa and $\tau_{xy} = 0$ MPa.

The normal stress at right angles to the grain is:

$$\sigma_\theta = \frac{1}{2}(6-14) + \frac{1}{2}(6+14)\cos 60° + 0$$
$$= -4 + (10 \times 0.5)$$
$$= 1 \text{ MPa}$$

and the shear stress in the direction of the grain is:

$$\tau_\theta = -\frac{1}{2}(6+14)\sin 60° + 0 = -10 \times 0.866 = -8.7 \text{ MPa}$$

SAQ 1.7

We are told to assume $\sigma_1 = 50$ MPa at failure. Given $\sigma_x = -10$ MPa and $\sigma_y = 35$ MPa, we can use Equation (1.9) to determine τ_{xy}:

$$50 = \frac{-10+35}{2} \pm \sqrt{\left(\frac{-10-35}{2}\right)^2 + \tau_{xy}^2}$$

$$50 = 12.5 \pm \sqrt{506.25 + \tau_{xy}^2}$$

$$37.5 = \pm\sqrt{506.25 + \tau_{xy}^2}$$

Square both sides:

$$1406.25 = 506.25 + \tau_{xy}^2$$

Thus:

$$\tau_{xy}^2 = 900 \text{ MPa}$$
$$\tau_{xy} = 30 \text{ MPa}$$

SAQ 1.8

(a) By inspection of the element: $\sigma_x = 30$ MPa, $\sigma_y = -60$ MPa, $\tau_{xy} = 20$ MPa and $\theta = -55°$.

The Mohr's circle is shown in Figure 1.80 with transformed diameter X'Y' drawn $2\theta = -110°$ (clockwise) with respect to the initial XY diameter.

X' at (−49, 35) MPa defines the stress components for the inclined section with $\sigma_{x'} = -49$ MPa, and $\tau_{x'y'} = 35$ MPa.

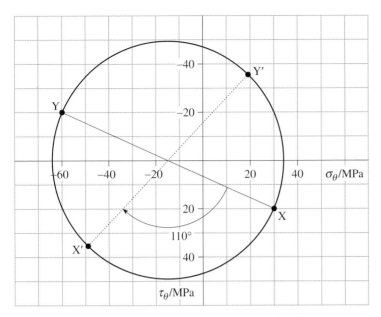

Figure 1.80   Mohr's circle for the stress element in Figure 1.65

(b) By inspection of the element: $\sigma_x = 30$ MPa, $\sigma_y = -60$ MPa, $\tau_{xy} = 20$ MPa and $\theta = -55°$.

Hence, using Equations (1.7) and (1.8):

$$\sigma_\theta = \frac{1}{2}(30 - 60) + \frac{1}{2}(30 + 60)\cos(-110°) + 20\sin(-110°)$$

$$= -15 - 15.39 - 18.79$$

$$= -49.2 \text{ MPa}$$

$$\tau_\theta = -\frac{1}{2}(30 + 60)\sin(-110°) + 20\cos(-110°)$$

$$= 42.29 - 6.84$$

$$= 35.4 \text{ MPa}$$

which confirms the answers from the Mohr's circle sketch used in part (a).

SAQ 1.9

(a) The stress state at A is close to uniaxial tension; only σ_y is significant. Hence, at A, $\sigma_1 \approx 50$ MPa, $\sigma_2 \approx 0$.

(b) The stress state at B is 'complex'; it involves biaxial tension plus shear.

The principal stresses and orientations at B are:

$$\sigma_{1,2} = \frac{\sigma_x + \sigma_y}{2} \pm \sqrt{\left(\frac{\sigma_x - \sigma_y}{2}\right)^2 + \tau_{xy}^2}$$

$$= \frac{14.7 + 52.6}{2} \pm \sqrt{\left(\frac{14.7 - 52.6}{2}\right)^2 + (-56.7)^2}$$

$$= 33.65 \pm 59.78 \text{ MPa}$$

That is, $\sigma_1 = 93$ MPa and $\sigma_2 = -26$ MPa.

$$\tan 2\theta_p = \frac{2\tau_{xy}}{\sigma_x - \sigma_y} = \frac{(2 \times -56.7)\,\text{MPa}}{(14.7 - 52.6)\,\text{MPa}} = 3.0$$

$$\theta_p = 35.8°, \ 125.8°$$

The maximum principal stress $\sigma_1 = 93$ MPa at $\theta_p = 125.8°$.

The minimum principal stress $\sigma_2 = -26$ MPa at $\theta_p = 35.8°$.

(c) Your graph should look something like Figure 1.81.

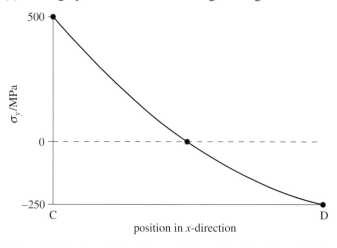

Figure 1.81   Graph showing variation of σ_y along line CD for the hook geometry

The y-direction stress goes from a maximum in tension at C, through zero at the approximate mid-thickness of the hook, then reaches a compressive minimum at D.

(d) Bending of the hook will place one edge (C) in tension and the other (D) in compression.

(e) It would be possible to reduce the stress around CD by making the hook thicker in this area: spreading the load reduces the stress.

ACKNOWLEDGEMENTS

Grateful acknowledgement is made to the following sources:

FIGURES

Figure 1.1: © Enigma/Alamy; © Tim Graham/Alamy; © Alt-6/Alamy; © archivberlin Fotoagentur GmbH/Alamy; © Willy Matheis l/Alamy.

Figure 1.2(a): © David R. Frazier Photolibrary, Inc./Alamy.

Figure 1.2(b): © Sequoia Aircraft Corporation.

Figure 1.6: Taken from www.merc.mercer.edu. Mercer Engineering Research Center.

Figure 1.10: © Alan Schein/Alamy.

Figure 1.11: From www.steelesolutions.com/photo_gallery.php

Fig 1.17: © Nordicphotos/Alamy; © Bettmann/Corbis.

Figure 1.28: Reproduced with kind permission of the Department of Materials Science & Metallurgy, University of Cambridge and courtesy of Dr S Tin (now of Illinois Institute of Technology).

Figure 1.40(a): © Chris Henderson/Construction Photography.

Figure 1.40(b): © Ted Kinsman/SPL.

Figure 1.40(c): © Ralph Hampton/Rex Features.

Figure 1.45: Roy E. Hanson Jnr. Mfg.

Figure 1.54: © Getty Images.

Figure 1.59: © Shotfile/Alamy.

Every effort has been made to contact copyright holders. If any have been inadvertently overlooked the publishers will be pleased to make the necessary arrangements at the first opportunity.

COURSE TEAM ACKNOWLEDGEMENTS

This part was prepared for the course team by Martin Rist with contributions by Michael Fitzpatrick.

CONTENTS

1   **THE CONCEPT OF STRAIN**   **105**

2   **NORMAL STRAIN**   **106**

3   **SHEAR STRAIN**   **112**

4   **PLANE STRAIN**   **116**

5   **RELATING STRAIN TO STRESS**   **119**

    5.1   Material properties   119

    5.2   Linear-elastic constitutive equations   122

6   **STRAIN MEASUREMENT: EXPERIMENTAL STRESS ANALYSIS**   **130**

    6.1   Photoelasticity   130

    6.2   The electrical resistance strain gauge   136

    6.3   Strain transformation   139

    6.4   Mohr's strain circle   141

    6.5   Rosette strain gauge analysis   143

7   **FREIGHT CONTAINER CASE STUDY**   **149**

8   **SUMMARY**   **158**

LEARNING OUTCOMES   **159**

ANSWERS TO EXERCISES   **160**

ANSWERS TO SELF-ASSESSMENT QUESTIONS   **164**

ACKNOWLEDGEMENTS   **173**

1 THE CONCEPT OF STRAIN

Up to this point we have restricted our study of structural integrity to understanding and quantifying stress (in a block entitled *Stress analysis* what else were you expecting?). Clearly, stress is important because without it a bicycle wheel wouldn't buckle, a cake-knife handle wouldn't snap and a suspension bridge wouldn't collapse. But it is not the whole story. Stress is a way of describing load intensity, and although all the examples of failure I've just quoted are a result of the stress exceeding some limit, the *deformation* associated with a failure can be just as important. Indeed, in some cases too much deformation can lead to a failure even though the stress is well within the strength of the material.

To describe deformation we need a means of quantifying dimensional changes in the size and shape of a material body; this is known as *strain* in engineering terminology.

A lift designer needs to know by just how much the cable is likely to stretch when the lift is full, else the lift may not line up properly at each floor. Old buildings (or poorly built new ones) can distort over time under relatively modest loads (Figure 2.1). And commonly in engineering, designers have to account for changes in dimension when components are heated, i.e. the effects of thermal expansion.

Figure 2.1   Old, timber-framed buildings often become distorted with age

2 NORMAL STRAIN

First, let's consider the deformation of a structure or material in response to loading in a single direction. The deformation of most engineering structures is small, and we would want it to be so, but it is easier to picture what is going on if the deformation is large, so I will use a stretchy rubber band (Figure 2.2a) as an example.

If I apply a uniaxial tensile load F by hanging a small weight on a rubber band, then there is likely to be an extension ΔL of its initial length L, as sketched in Figure 2.2(b). Now, if I were to connect two identical rubber bands together and hang the same weight off the bottom band, then *both* bands would experience the same force F and so *each* would stretch by the same amount, i.e. ΔL (Figure 2.2c). The *total* extension in this case would be $2\Delta L$. Similarly, three identical rubber bands connected end to end under the same load would stretch $3\Delta L$, and so on. The important thing here is that the extension is proportional to the initial dimension: length L extends to $L + \Delta L$, $2L$ to $2L + 2\Delta L$, $3L$ to $3L + 3\Delta L$, etc. This means that the *ratio* of extension to unstressed length is the same for all three cases, $\Delta L/L = 2\Delta L/2L = 3\Delta L/3L$, and would be the same for any initial length and tensile force F; the ratio depends only on the stress and the type of material.

This ratio $\Delta L/L$ is called the *normal strain* (or *direct strain*), and is usually represented by ε, the Greek letter epsilon. In other words, the normal strain ε is the fractional increase in length:

$$\varepsilon = \frac{\Delta L}{L} \tag{2.1}$$

Because strain is the ratio of two lengths it has no units (the units are effectively metres divided by metres, which cancel out), so we call it a *dimensionless* quantity.

Figure 2.2 Rubber bands under tensile load

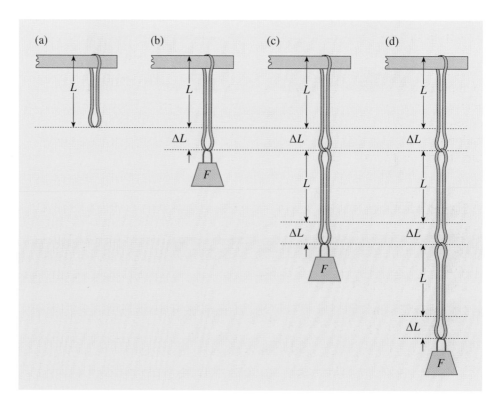

EXAMPLE

The shaft of a steel 'connecting rod' in a car engine experiences alternating compressive and tensile stresses when it is pushed and pulled by the movement of the piston during the engine's combustion cycle. If these stresses cause the shaft length, initially 125.000 mm, to alternately increase to 125.100 mm and decrease to 124.875 mm, what strain is reached during the tensile and compressive parts of the cycle?

SOLUTION

In tension the change in length is from 125.000 mm to 125.100 mm, hence:

$$\varepsilon = \frac{\Delta L}{L}$$

$$= \frac{125.100 \text{ mm} - 125.000 \text{ mm}}{125.000 \text{ mm}}$$

$$= 0.0008$$

In compression the change in length is −0.125 mm (always subtract the *initial* length from the *final* length to get ΔL), so:

$$\varepsilon = \frac{\Delta L}{L}$$

$$= \frac{-0.125 \text{ mm}}{125 \text{ mm}}$$

$$= -0.001$$

Note from the last example that contractions in length, associated with compressive (i.e. negative) normal stresses, give rise to negative normal strains. Also, most strains associated with engineering analysis are quite small. As a result, it is common to multiply them by 100 to present them as a percentage: hence a strain of 0.0008 is equivalent to a strain of 0.08%. This usually has the advantage of reducing the number of zeros you have to mouth when you say a strain value. Another approach is to multiply the strain by 10^6 and refer to it as 'microstrain', sometimes abbreviated to '$\mu\varepsilon$'. In this case, a strain of 0.0008 is equivalent to $800\mu\varepsilon$.

EXERCISE 2.1

In order to measure the strain in a metal bar of length 300 mm, an engineer carefully marked the position of two 'gauge points' on the bar, initially 100 mm apart. Under tensile loading applied at the ends of the bar, the separation of these points increased by 0.1 mm.

(a) Determine the strain in the bar and express it as an absolute value, a percentage and a microstrain.

(b) Estimate the total length of the stressed bar.

SAQ 2.1 (Learning outcome 2.1)

A square aluminium support column of side 50 mm and length 2.0 m is loaded by an axial compressive force of 130 kN. If the strain is measured to be −0.0007, determine:

(a) the final length of the column

(b) the normal stress along its length.

Although most common structural materials, including metal and concrete, exhibit very small strains in normal service, other materials, such as polyethylene and rubber, can be deformed to strains of 300% or more. Large strains, over 100%, also occur during specialized metal-forming processes, such as wire drawing and forging, which are often carried out at high temperatures where the metal has a much lower resistance to deformation. The analysis of such deformations exposes a limitation to the use of the formula for strain presented in Equation (2.1), usually referred to as *engineering strain*, of which you should be aware. To illustrate the problem, consider the following exercise.

EXERCISE 2.2

A block of rubber is stretched from 10 cm to 13 cm long.

(a) Calculate the strain according to the formula for engineering strain $\varepsilon = \Delta L/L$.

(b) Repeat the calculation for a compression from 13 cm back to 10 cm.

The answer to Exercise 2.2 demonstrates that applying the definition $\varepsilon = \Delta L/L$ can give different values of strain in tension and compression. Although this might seem rather unsatisfactory, it is actually a problem only at large strains; at low values of strain (i.e. <0.1 or 10%) the difference is negligible. To produce a definition of strain that gives the same magnitude(but opposite sign) for large tensile and compressive strains it is necessary to use ☑ **true strain** ☑, sometimes called 'logarithmic strain'. However, the strains encountered during stress analysis of engineering components and structures are usually well below 10%, and more typically of the order of 0.1%, and so the use of the engineering definition of strain is perfectly adequate.

Now, if you have ever stretched a rubber band to any great length you will have seen that it also gets thinner (Figure 2.3). In other words, you already know that a normal stress doesn't generate strain only in the same direction as the applied load. Figure 2.4 shows a rectangular bar of material subjected to a tensile stress σ_x in the *x*-direction, parallel to the long bar axis. As we have seen, the associated normal strain ε_x in the *x*-direction can be determined from the ratio of extension ΔL to the original length:

$$\varepsilon_x = \frac{\Delta L}{L}$$

☑ True strain

True strain is more useful and more accurate than engineering strain for describing large strains. To understand true strain it is necessary to consider a large strain to be the summation of a sequence of small strains:

$$\varepsilon = \sum \frac{\Delta L}{L}$$

In mathematical notation this is the same as integrating (or summing) many infinitesimally small lengths, size dL, over the entire length L:

$$\varepsilon = \int \frac{\mathrm{d}L}{L}$$

For a change in length from L_0 to L_1 it is necessary to carry out this integration between limits:

$$\varepsilon = \int_{L_0}^{L_1} \frac{\mathrm{d}L}{L} = \int_{L_0}^{L_1} \frac{1}{L} \mathrm{d}L = {}_{L_0}^{L_1}\big[\ln L\big] = \big[\ln L_1 - \ln L_0\big] = \ln \frac{L_1}{L_0}$$

You can skip over this maths if you are not used to integrating between limits; it's the final result that is important.

Hence, analysing strain in this way leads to the definition of true strain:

$$\varepsilon = \ln \frac{L_1}{L_0} \qquad\qquad (2.2)$$

where L_0 is the original length, L_1 is the final length and 'ln' denotes 'natural logarithm' (also called 'logarithm to base e' or 'log$_e$'). The extent of the effect can be appreciated by looking at the calculations displayed in Table 2.1.

Table 2.1   Comparison between engineering strain and true strain

$\dfrac{L_1}{L_0}$	Engineering strain (tension) $\dfrac{L_1 - L_0}{L_0}$	Engineering strain (compression) $\dfrac{L_1 - L_0}{L_0}$	Logarithmic strain $\ln \dfrac{L_1}{L_0}$
1.01	0.010	−0.010	0.010
1.10	0.100	−0.091	0.095
1.20	0.200	−0.167	0.182
1.50	0.500	−0.333	0.405

Up to about 10% strain, differences between engineering and logarithmic strains are small. Above this value the difference becomes more and more evident.

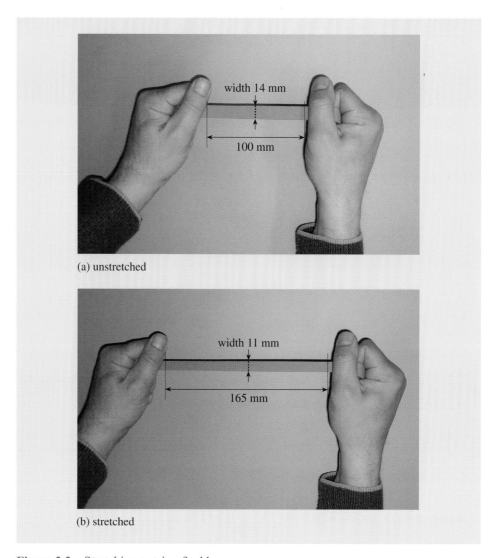

(a) unstretched

(b) stretched

Figure 2.3   Stretching a strip of rubber

But the bar will also exhibit a contraction in its lateral dimensions, so that its width w decreases by an amount Δw and there is a strain in the y-direction:

$$\varepsilon_y = \frac{\Delta w}{w}$$

Recall that because Δw represents a reduction in the material dimension, we assign it a negative value. Hence, in Figure 2.4 the material has experienced a positive direct strain in the x-direction and a negative one in the y-direction. Note that, in three dimensions, there will also be a negative strain ε_z in the z-direction. This change of dimension in a direction perpendicular to the applied load is known as the Poisson effect, named after the French polymath Siméon-Denis Poisson (Figure 2.5). The Poisson strain occurs in the y- and z-directions even though there is no applied stress in those directions.

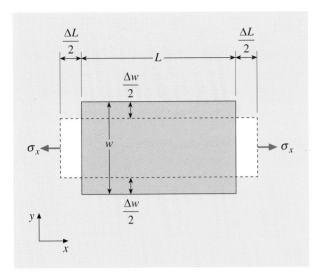

Figure 2.4   Rectangular bar under uniaxial stress

Figure 2.5   Siméon-Denis Poisson

SAQ 2.2 (Learning outcome 2.1)

Referring to the dimensional changes that occur when the rubber band shown in Figure 2.3 is deformed in uniaxial tension, calculate:

(a) the average longitudinal and lateral *engineering* strains

(b) the average longitudinal and lateral *true* strains

in the stretched rubber band.

3 SHEAR STRAIN

Normal stresses, tensile and compressive, give rise to extensions and contractions in the linear dimensions of a material body. Shear stresses, however, do not produce direct strains of this kind. Take a look at Figure 2.6(a), which shows a rectangular piece of material with a square grid marked on it. The material is subjected to shear stresses as shown. The effect of this stress is to cause an angular deformation that distorts the squares into parallelograms, as illustrated in Figure 2.6(b). The internal angles of the grid, initially 90°, now become either $(90° - \gamma)$, or $(90° + \gamma)$ where γ (the Greek letter gamma) represents the change in angle from the initial right angle. The deformation illustrated in Figure 2.6 has been exaggerated for clarity, but the important thing to notice is that, under pure shear, *the lengths of the grid lines have not changed*, only the angles between them.

Now let's consider how to describe this shear deformation a little more rigorously. I have rotated and redrawn the deformed grid of Figure 2.6(b) for clarity in Figure 2.7. I have also added an *xy*-coordinate frame of reference and have shown the applied shear stress $\tau_{xy} (= \tau_{yx})$ that generated the deformation. It is usual to label the angular change with subscripts that are the same as those of the shear stress that caused it, so I have now labelled the angle as γ_{xy}. Figure 2.7 shows that the applied shear stress has caused a displacement d at the corner A, relative to the origin O. Evidently, if A had been further from the origin to begin with, then d would have been larger – twice as large if A had been twice as far from the origin. For a meaningful definition of shear strain, then, it makes sense to divide d by the distance h from the origin. This d/h ratio is the tangent of the angle γ_{xy} (Figure 2.7), but for small angles measured in radians the tangent of any angle is approximately equal to the angle itself (you can prove this to yourself with a calculator). Again, it turns out that such an approximation is a good one for the small deformations usually analysed in engineering structural design; typically, γ is less than 0.001. Hence, for our purposes, the angular deformation γ_{xy}, measured in radians, *defines* the shear strain:

There are 2π radians in a circle, which must be equivalent to 360°, so to convert from degrees to radians, multiply by $2\pi/360$.

$$\gamma_{xy} = \frac{d}{h}$$

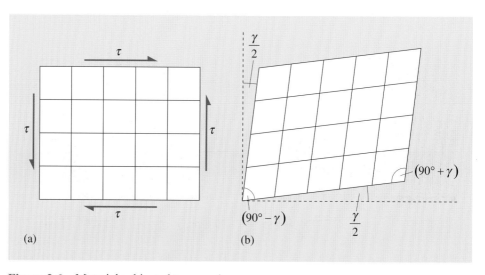

(a)

(b)

Figure 2.6   Material subjected to pure shear

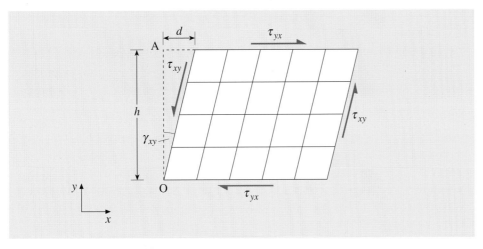

Figure 2.7   Redrawn deformed grid

So you can think of shear strain either as an angular change or as the ratio of deformation to original dimensions. Shear strains associated with positive shear stresses are defined to be positive; those associated with negative shear stresses are negative.

EXERCISE 2.3

In Figure 2.7, what are the signs of τ_{xy}, τ_{yx} and γ_{xy}?

We can extend our description of shear strain to three dimensions by imagining the piece of material in Figure 2.7 as a rectangular prism that has undergone angular distortion between *all three* pairs of its faces; see Figure 2.8. In this case there are three independent angular changes, γ_{xy}, γ_{yz} and γ_{zx} caused, respectively, by the three independent shear stresses τ_{xy}, τ_{yz} and τ_{zx}.

If we now consider an infinitesimally small element of material (like the prism of Figure 2.8, but smaller) then we have the means to describe fully the three-dimensional

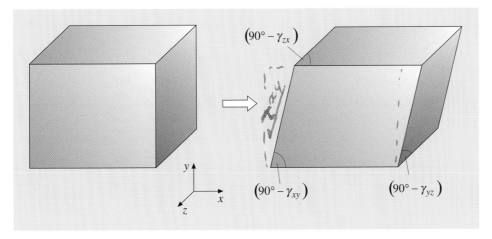

Figure 2.8   Element distorted under three-dimensional shear strain

state of strain at a point. Grouping the components into a *tensor*, just as we did for stress in Block 1 Part 1, gives:

$$\begin{bmatrix} \varepsilon_x & \gamma_{xy} & \gamma_{xz} \\ \gamma_{yx} & \varepsilon_y & \gamma_{yz} \\ \gamma_{zx} & \gamma_{zy} & \varepsilon_z \end{bmatrix}$$

where $\gamma_{xy} = \gamma_{yx}$, $\gamma_{yz} = \gamma_{zy}$ and $\gamma_{zx} = \gamma_{xz}$, analogous to the equivalence of the shear stress tensor components. As for stress, the complete three-dimensional description of strain requires three independent normal strains, ε_x, ε_y and ε_z, and three independent shear strains, γ_{xy}, γ_{yz} and γ_{xz}, i.e. six in total. Fortunately, many common engineering problems can be tackled using a two-dimensional simplification of a three-dimensional reality, as we shall see next.

Both the examples of strain I have introduced so far are strains that occur in response to an applied stress. But it is possible for a material to change its dimensions without any stress being applied. Before moving on to the next section, read ☑ **Thermal strains and other stress-free strains** ☑.

☑ Thermal strains and other stress-free strains

The most obvious example of this is *thermal expansion*. When a material is heated its dimensions increase – by a small amount, but significant if the temperature change is large.

This is quantified by the *coefficient of thermal expansion* (CTE), some values of which are shown in Table 2.2. Values of CTE are generally expressed as strain per degree Celsius temperature change. For example, aluminium has a CTE of $24 \times 10^{-6}\ °C^{-1}$, which means that it experiences a strain of $24\mu\varepsilon$ for each degree Celsius rise in temperature. So a 1 m bar will increase in length by 24 μm if the temperature rises by 1 °C.

This can be written mathematically as:

$$\Delta L = L_0 \alpha \Delta T \tag{2.3}$$

where ΔL is the change in length, L_0 is the original length, α is the coefficient of thermal expansion and ΔT is the change in temperature.

And as strain is defined as the change in length divided by the original length, it follows that:

$$\varepsilon = \alpha \Delta T$$

Table 2.2   Values of coefficient of thermal expansion

Material	CTE/$10^{-6}\ °C^{-1}$
Aluminium	24
Brass	19
Copper	17
Concrete	12
Glass	9
Nickel	13
Steel	10–13 (varies with composition)
Stainless steel	17

Thermal expansion occurs equally in all the dimensions of a component, and leads to linear changes in all directions. As a result, the CTE is sometimes called the coefficient of linear thermal expansion.

EXAMPLE

Take as an example polyacetal, which is used in many kettle bodies. It has a CTE of $80 \times 10^{-6}\ °C^{-1}$. So what will the increase in height be for a kettle of initial height 250 mm when it heats water from 15 °C to 100 °C?

SOLUTION

Using Equation (2.3), and assuming that the body of the kettle is at the same temperature as the water:

$$\Delta L = 0.25 \text{ m} \times 80 \times 10^{-6} \text{ °C}^{-1} \times 85 \text{ °C}$$
$$= 1.7 \times 10^{-3} \text{ m or } 1.7 \text{ mm}$$

The example shows that thermal expansions can be measurable and significant. Now try SAQ 2.3.

SAQ 2.3 (Learning outcome 2.9)

A turbine blade in a jet engine is 120 mm long and is made from a nickel alloy with a CTE of $15 \times 10^{-6} \text{ °C}^{-1}$. In operation it may be heated from 0 °C to 850 °C. Calculate the change in length of the blade.

Thermal strains are 'stress-free' strains: although heating or cooling causes a change in dimensions, there isn't any applied stress involved. However, if whatever is being heated (or cooled) is prevented from expanding (or contracting) by clamping or some other force, perhaps by being joined to something with a lower CTE that isn't deforming as much, then an external stress will be associated with the strain in the same way as with normal loading, and this can lead to failure. See for example the railway lines in Figure 2.9, where sufficient stress was generated by solar heating to cause buckling.

Other sources of stress-free strains include transformation strains, where changes in the structure of a material are coupled with a change in dimension. During the heat treatment of steels there

Figure 2.9 Buckled railway rails

are phase changes which, if not accounted for, can generate sufficient stress to crack the component being treated. This is particularly the case during quenching – rapid cooling in water or oil – of hardenable steels where the formation of the hard martensite phase involves a volume increase which can cause cracking if the quench rate is too severe or if the component is unevenly cooled.

4 PLANE STRAIN

In many three-dimensional engineering structures, physical constraints prevent significant strain occurring in a particular direction, allowing the analysis to be reduced to a simpler two-dimensional problem, that of *plane strain*. Think of a cube of material that is constrained between two fixed rigid blocks as drawn in Figure 2.10(a). If a compressive stress is applied in a horizontal direction, then the cube is prevented from expanding vertically by the constraining blocks. Under such circumstances it is usual to define the z-direction as that in which no deformation takes place; hence $\varepsilon_z = 0$. Further, if loading is evenly distributed, then uniform deformation should take place only along the xy-planes (Figure 2.10b), so there is no component of deformation in the z-direction at all; hence $\gamma_{yz} = \gamma_{zx} = 0$. The only remaining non-zero components are the direct strains ε_x and ε_y, and the shear strain γ_{xy}.

Although the displacements and strains in the z-direction are zero, this does not mean that the stress in the z-direction is also zero. Consider again the compressive stress σ_y acting alone in Figure 2.10(b). Recall that such loading ought to create a lateral expansion strain ε_z. This doesn't happen in Figure 2.10, because the immoveable blocks provide a reaction force that prevents the expansion. In other words, a stress σ_z is necessary to maintain the $\varepsilon_z = 0$ condition.

The plane strain condition acts as a useful approximation to many real loading situations even when there is no apparent external constraint. In particular, it is common to apply plane strain to a structure that is very long in one dimension and that experiences uniform loading perpendicular to its length. In such structures, it can be assumed that there is no significant strain in the z-direction because the *material itself* provides the constraint. Take, for example, the schematic diagram of a gravity dam shown in Figure 2.11. The idea is that the sheer length of the dam means that any deformation along its length is effectively negligible, and so deformation is constrained to planes parallel to the shaded xy-plane in this figure. As above, only the direct strains ε_x and ε_y and the shear strain γ_{xy} can exist in this plane.

As well as dams, plane strain analysis is commonly applied to internally pressurized pipes or externally loaded tunnels, for example. In any case, such analysis is most effective if it is restricted to the mid-length of the structure (i.e. well away from its ends, where the constraining effect may be less valid).

Figure 2.10   Plane strain in a constrained cube of material

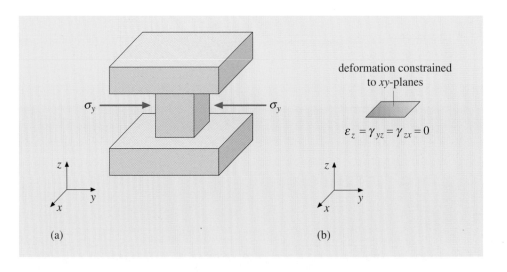

(a)

deformation constrained to xy-planes

$\varepsilon_z = \gamma_{yz} = \gamma_{zx} = 0$

(b)

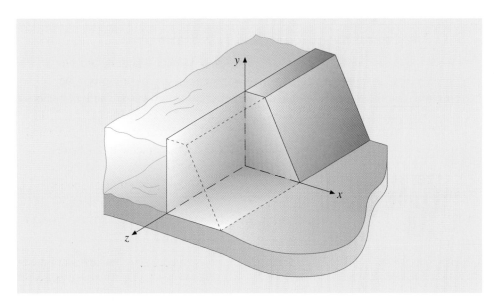

Figure 2.11   Gravity dam

Plane strain can be considered as the other extreme to the condition of plane stress, for which the stress components in the z-direction are zero, i.e. $\sigma_z = \tau_{xz} = \tau_{yz} = 0$. Recall from Part 1 that plane stress is often applied to the analysis of the stress state in the plane of a surface, or within unbounded thin sheets, since stress must be zero normal to a free surface. However, be careful to note that under plane stress there usually *will* be a strain, ε_z, in the z-direction due to lateral contraction or expansion. To help distinguish between the two, see the summary ☑ **Plane strain and plane stress** ☑.

Plane stress was introduced in Block 1 Part 1, Section 5.1.

☑ Plane strain and plane stress

Plane strain can be considered to occur in bodies that are long in one direction, say z:

$$\varepsilon_x \neq 0 \qquad \varepsilon_y \neq 0 \qquad \gamma_{xy} \neq 0$$
$$\varepsilon_z = 0 \qquad \gamma_{zx} = 0 \qquad \gamma_{yz} = 0$$

In tensor form the non-zero components of plane strain can be written as:

$$\begin{bmatrix} \varepsilon_x & \gamma_{xy} \\ \gamma_{yx} & \varepsilon_y \end{bmatrix}$$

A 2×2 tensor can be used because the other components are zero. The full tensor would look like:

$$\begin{bmatrix} \varepsilon_x & \gamma_{xy} & 0 \\ \gamma_{yx} & \varepsilon_y & 0 \\ 0 & 0 & 0 \end{bmatrix}$$

Plane stress can be considered to occur in bodies that are thin in one direction, say z:

$$\sigma_x \neq 0 \qquad \sigma_y \neq 0 \qquad \tau_{xy} \neq 0$$
$$\sigma_z = 0 \qquad \tau_{zx} = 0 \qquad \tau_{yz} = 0$$

In tensor form the non-zero components of plane stress can be written as:

$$\begin{bmatrix} \sigma_x & \tau_{xy} \\ \tau_{yx} & \sigma_y \end{bmatrix}$$

with the other components being equal to zero.

SAQ 2.4 (Learning outcomes 2.1, 2.3 and 2.4)

A rapidly spinning turbine disc, used for holding the rotating blades in a gas turbine aero-engine, is loaded by inertia forces as shown in Figure 2.12. Assuming that the thickness of the disc is small compared with its other dimensions, deduce whether the disc can be idealized as being in a state of plane stress or plane strain.

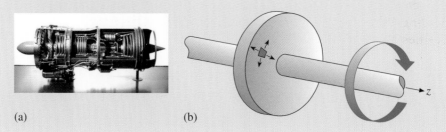

(a)   (b)

Figure 2.12   (a) Cut-away of an aircraft jet engine showing the internal array of turbine discs and blades attached to a central shaft; (b) idealized geometry of a single, spinning turbine disc

SAQ 2.5 (Learning outcomes 2.1, 2.3 and 2.4)

A sheet of steel is hot-rolled as shown in Figure 2.13. Assume that the rolling process is designed to reduce the thickness of the sheet markedly, but does not cause any significant lateral spreading of the metal (in fact this is a common simplifying assumption in the analysis of this type of metal processing). Deduce whether the sheet is in a state of plane stress or plane strain during forming.

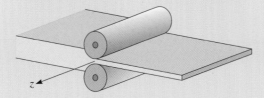

Figure 2.13   Material passing through a rolling mill

5 RELATING STRAIN TO STRESS

So far in Part 2 you have seen how to use strain as a means of describing deformation in a stressed material. However, we have not yet developed any direct quantitative relationships between stress and strain. Such formulations are called *constitutive equations*, and without them it is impossible to say how much deformation results from a given amount of stress, for example. The key ingredient in constructing a set of constitutive equations is an understanding of the way that a material responds to loading. Hence, to relate stress to strain it is first necessary to introduce material properties into our analysis.

5.1 Material properties

Useful design information for structural materials is conventionally obtained from carefully controlled tensile and compressive testing of sample lengths of material, using apparatus of the type shown in Figure 2.14. Usually, a test specimen is subjected to a uniaxial force in the direction of its longitudinal axis, and the load and strain acting over a prescribed 'gauge length' are measured. From these data, an average direct stress is computed, and assumed to apply uniformly over the cross section of the specimen. Graphs of stress against strain can then be plotted.

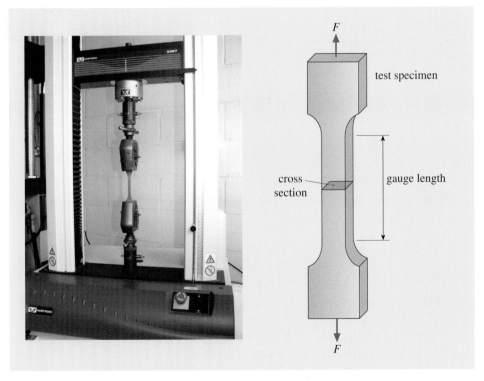

DVD

Tensile testing is covered in the 'Testing of materials and structures' programme on the DVD.

Figure 2.14   Materials testing machine and tensile test-piece

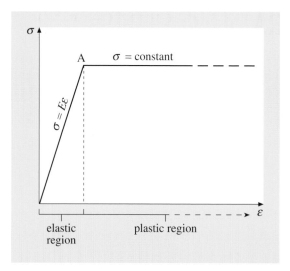

Figure 2.15   Idealized stress–strain behaviour for a structural material

Figure 2.15 shows an idealized version of what might be expected from many structural materials, particularly metals, during testing under uniaxial tension. There is initially an *elastic* region in which, if the stress is removed, the deformation will go back to zero – that is, it is *recoverable*. This elastic region is *linear*, so stress and strain bear a constant relationship to one another, given by $\sigma = E\varepsilon$, where E is Young's modulus; thus, stress is directly proportional to strain. At point A the material can withstand no further increase in stress, and enters a *plastic* region in which the material is no longer elastic and deforms indefinitely under the action of this maximum stress.

For the purposes of stress analysis, this simplified behaviour provides the basis for constructing a useful model of the way that structural materials behave under load. However, you should be aware that in practice things are not quite so simple, and real materials behave differently in various ways. Figure 2.16 shows three different types of stress–strain relationship for some typical metals used in structural engineering.

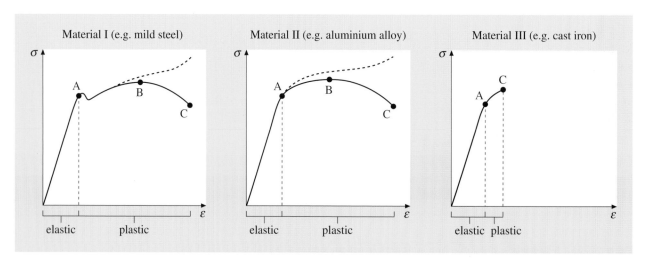

Figure 2.16   Different types of stress–strain curve, typical of some structural materials

These curves were produced from metal samples undergoing tensile testing, being gradually loaded until fracture occurred. Other materials will have differently shaped graphs.

All three of the materials represented in Figure 2.16 exhibit an elastic region, which is approximately linear, and a plastic region, but have no instantaneous change from one mode to the other. This transition from elastic to plastic behaviour is called *yield*, and can be associated with a sudden stress drop or *yield point*, as in material I, or be more gradual, as in materials II and III. Regardless of the nature of the transition, engineers often use a single figure, quoted as the *yield stress*. However, particularly for those materials not exhibiting a well-defined transition from elastic to plastic behaviour, it is more common to quote a *proof stress*. The proof stress is the stress that causes a specified permanent strain after the stress is removed. It is usually a standard permanent 'set' of 0.1% or 0.2% (i.e. $\varepsilon = 0.001$ or 0.002) and the proof stress will be quoted as, for example, 200 MPa, 0.1% proof.

For materials I and II, point B on the stress–strain curves is the measured maximum tensile stress, computed by dividing the load carried by the original cross-sectional area of the test piece. This stress is called the *ultimate tensile stress* (UTS). In practice, owing to substantial thinning of the specimen dimensions in the plastic region, there is a reduction in cross-sectional area. Hence, the actual material stress is higher, following the dashed line. In engineering practice the UTS is widely quoted, however, and is sometimes simply called the *tensile strength*.

Point C on each curve is where each of the three samples fractured and is usually known as the *failure stress* or *fracture stress*. The behaviour of materials I and II is said to be *ductile* because there is significant plastic deformation before failure, whereas material III has behaved in a *brittle* manner, with very little plastic strain following yield.

Materials property data are available in the technical literature, handbooks, and from material suppliers. Representative mechanical properties for a few materials are given in Table 2.3; good handbooks will give more detailed information.

Note that materials do not necessarily behave the same in compression as in tension. For example, the failure stress of wood is rather lower in compression. On the other hand, concrete is good in compression, but is generally considered to have negligible tensile strength – hence the common use of reinforced concrete, with steel bars to take tensile forces. The Young's modulus of most materials, including most metals, can be considered to be the same in tension and compression, although in the case of wood it is usually lower in compression.

Try, for example, *Smithells Metals Reference Book* (published by Butterworth-Heinemann) or the *ASM Metals Reference Book* (ASM International).

Table 2.3   Typical material properties

Material	Yield point or 0.1% proof stress/MPa	Ultimate strength/ MPa	Young's modulus/ GPa	Shear modulus/ GPa
Mild steel (hot rolled)	275	455	203	80
Carbon steel (hot rolled)	360	590	206	81
Alloy steel (high grade)	1310	1720	206	79
Cast iron:				
tension	~120	140	80	32
compression	~120	605	80	32
Stainless steel	1100	1275	190	86
Aluminium alloy	250	317	70	27
Magnesium alloy	240	338	45	17
Titanium alloy	896	1020	105	39
Concrete:				
tension	~4	~6	~15	~6
compression	40	60	19	~8
Glass, borosilicate (Pyrex®)	–	70	70	30
Silicon nitride (hot pressed)	–	900	305	120
Wood:				
fir (along grain)	55	124	14	~7
oak (along grain)	59	131	12	~8
balsa (along grain)	~18	~24	~4	~2
balsa (across grain)	~1	~1	~4	~2
Polyethylene	10	15	2	1
Poly(vinyl chloride)	42	46	3	~1
Polycarbonate	62	68	2	~1
Poly(methyl methacrylate)	~80	110	3	~1

5.2 Linear-elastic constitutive equations

In general, for structural analysis, the most basic material property assumption is that the material response is linear and elastic. This is a reasonable assumption for most metals below their yield stress, although at higher stresses they will eventually behave in a plastic manner and lose their load-bearing capability. Hence, the usual objective in the design of structures is to make sure that all stresses stay within the linear-elastic region, well below the yield stress, so that the structure can safely carry its loads over a period of time.

In using a linear-elastic model we assume that all stresses and strains are linearly dependent on the applied loads. Thus, no matter how complicated an internal pattern of stresses and strains may be, if the loads are increased by, say, 10% then so will be the stresses and strains. You have already seen (Figure 2.16) that for simple uniaxial loading, provided deformation remains linear-elastic, the stress is directly proportional to strain (this is known as *Hooke's law*, after seventeenth-century scientist Robert Hooke; Figure 2.17), so we can write:

$$\text{stress} = (\text{a constant}) \times \text{strain}$$

The constant of proportionality is known as the *modulus of elasticity* or *Young's modulus E*, and so for direct stresses and strains:

$$\sigma = E\varepsilon \tag{2.4}$$

Because strain is a dimensionless quantity, Equation (2.4) indicates that E must have the same units as stress, i.e. N m^{-2} or Pa.

The elastic modulus is often spoken of as the 'stiffness' of a material, and a stiff material means that a large stress is needed for a given strain, i.e. the material has a large value of E.

Torsion tests, in which cylindrical specimens are twisted about their axes, indicate that the linearity between stress and strain for elastic deformation also applies to shear stress and strain, but with a different constant of proportionality:

$$\tau = G\gamma \tag{2.5}$$

where G is the *shear modulus* or *modulus of rigidity*.

Figure 2.17   Robert Hooke (1635–1703)

Hooke proposed *ut tensio, sic vis*: 'as the extension, the force'. When he initially made the discovery he did not want to publish it immediately, so published an anagram of it – ceiiinosssttuv – and revealed the solution later.

Strictly speaking, 'stiffness' refers to the properties of a component, which are a combination of the material's properties and the component geometry. It is possible to make a component stiffer by making it thicker, for example, without changing the material.

EXAMPLE

A structural member made of an aluminium alloy and subject to simple uniaxial tension has a uniform cross-sectional area of 4×10^{-4} m^2 and a length of 0.9 m. Using the data of Table 2.3, estimate the greatest load that the member can carry without yielding, and the extension of the member at that load.

SOLUTION

Let's assume the greatest acceptable load F corresponds to the yield stress (strictly speaking it is just below this). For an aluminium alloy this stress is 250 MPa; thus:

$$\text{load } F = \sigma A = 250 \times 10^6 \text{ N m}^{-2} \times 4 \times 10^{-4} \text{ m} = 100 \text{ kN}$$

The Young's modulus E for this material is 70 GPa; therefore:

$$\text{strain } \varepsilon = \frac{\sigma}{E} = \frac{250 \times 10^6 \text{ Pa}}{70 \times 10^9 \text{ Pa}} = 3.57 \times 10^{-3}$$

and

$$\text{extension } \Delta L = \varepsilon L = 3.57 \times 10^{-3} \times 0.9 \text{ m} = 0.0032 \text{ m} = 3.2 \text{ mm}$$

EXERCISE 2.4

A concrete column has a cross-sectional area of 0.1 m^2 and is 10 m in length. If it were to carry a stress equal to one half of its ultimate compressive strength, estimate the change in length.

SAQ 2.6 (Learning outcomes 2.1, 2.2 and 2.6)

A 2 km long mine hoist cable made of alloy steel has a cross-sectional area of 300 mm².

(a) Estimate the extension of the cable when it carries a load of 3000 kg.

(b) Estimate the contraction of the cable assuming that its entire length is cooled from 20 °C to 5 °C as it is lowered into the mine. Assume the steel has a CTE of 10×10^{-6} °C^{-1}.

Throughout this course, unless stated otherwise, it is assumed that the structural materials under consideration have properties that do not vary from one point to another, and that the properties are the same in all directions from a point. That is to say, each material is homogeneous and isotropic.

Recall that, because of the Poisson effect, a body deforming under load experiences a normal strain component parallel to the direction of loading and lateral strains at right angles to this. In practice, for linear-elastic materials that are also homogeneous and isotropic, it has been found that the lateral strain bears a particular constant relationship to the strain parallel to the direction of loading. For example, if a uniaxial tensile stress σ_x produces a strain $\varepsilon_x = \sigma_x/E$ in the x-direction, then the lateral strains ε_y and ε_z are directly proportional to ε_x:

$$\varepsilon_y = \varepsilon_z = -\nu\varepsilon_x$$

or

$$\varepsilon_y = \varepsilon_z = -\nu\left(\frac{\sigma_x}{E}\right)$$

where ν is a material-dependent constant of proportionality known as *Poisson's ratio*. The negative sign appears because a positive extension in the x-direction must lead to a negative contraction in the y- and z-directions, and vice versa. Because strain is a dimensionless quantity, ν is also dimensionless and, for most metals, has a value of about 0.3 for elastic deformations.

EXERCISE 2.5

A steel bar supports a uniaxial tensile stress of 100 MPa. What axial and lateral strains does it experience? (Assume $E = 210$ GPa, $\nu = 0.3$.)

It is a simple matter to deduce strains for uniaxial stresses aligned along the other coordinate axes. An element subjected to a uniaxial stress σ_y will undergo a strain $\varepsilon_y = \sigma_y/E$ in the y-direction, and lateral strains ε_x and ε_z (equal to $-\nu\sigma_y/E$) in the x- and z-directions. Similarly, an element subjected to a uniaxial stress σ_z will undergo a strain $\varepsilon_z = \sigma_z/E$ in the z-direction, and lateral contractions ε_x and ε_y (equal to $-\nu\sigma_z/E$) in the x- and y-directions.

I have gone through these uniaxial expressions relating normal and lateral strain components one by one because they supply us with enough ammunition to build a full set of stress–strain equations in three dimensions. In fact, the distribution of stresses and strains due to simple loading conditions can be added, or *superimposed*, to reproduce the effect caused by more complicated loading. Expressed more formally, for small linear-elastic deformations the *principle of superposition* states that 'If a material body is subjected to two or more stresses, the strain produced by each of the stresses is the same as if the other stresses were absent.'

EXAMPLE

Deduce the total x-direction strain ε_x, in terms of stress, for an elastic element subjected to three normal stresses, σ_x, σ_y and σ_z, simultaneously.

SOLUTION

The x-direction strains are:

σ_x/E due to σ_x

$-v\sigma_y/E$ due to σ_y

$-v\sigma_z/E$ due to σ_z.

Adding these three strains together gives:

$$\varepsilon_x = \frac{\sigma_x}{E} - \frac{v\sigma_y}{E} - \frac{v\sigma_z}{E}$$

$$= \frac{\sigma_x}{E} - \frac{v}{E}\left(\sigma_y + \sigma_z\right)$$

The procedure followed in the last example can be carried out for all three coordinate directions to obtain equations relating stress and strain in three dimensions. These are:

$$\varepsilon_x = \frac{\sigma_x}{E} - \frac{v}{E}\left(\sigma_y + \sigma_z\right) \tag{2.6}$$

$$\varepsilon_y = \frac{\sigma_y}{E} - \frac{v}{E}\left(\sigma_x + \sigma_z\right) \tag{2.7}$$

$$\varepsilon_z = \frac{\sigma_z}{E} - \frac{v}{E}\left(\sigma_x + \sigma_y\right) \tag{2.8}$$

To complete this set of constitutive equations we can take account of the fact that there is no Poisson effect for shear strain; hence, from Equation (2.5):

$$\gamma_{xy} = \frac{\tau_{xy}}{G}, \; \gamma_{yz} = \frac{\tau_{yz}}{G}, \; \gamma_{zx} = \frac{\tau_{zx}}{G} \tag{2.9}$$

Equations (2.6)–(2.9) express all six independent strain components in terms of the six independent stress components, and incorporate three elastic constants E, G and v. For a particular material these elastic constants are related by a useful expression, independent of stress and strain:

$$G = \frac{E}{2(1+v)} \tag{2.10}$$

※ what can this tell us

Note that two-dimensional constitutive equations for normal strains can be obtained from Equations (2.6)–(2.8) by simply setting one of the stress components, usually σ_z, equal to zero.

EXAMPLE

A three-dimensional element of steel experiences a complex state of stress with $\sigma_x = -90$ MPa and $\sigma_y = 30$ MPa. Strain in the z-direction is effectively prevented by the nature of the structure, i.e. the element is in plane strain. Determine the stress in the z-direction and the strain in the x- and y-directions ($E = 210$ GPa, $v = 0.3$).

SOLUTION

Given $\sigma_x = -90$ MPa, $\sigma_y = 30$ MPa and $\varepsilon_z = 0$ (plane strain), we can use Equation (2.8) to obtain σ_z. It is usually simpler to rearrange the equation before inserting the values:

$$\varepsilon_z = \frac{\sigma_z}{E} - \frac{v}{E}\left(\sigma_x + \sigma_y\right)$$

$$E\varepsilon_z = \sigma_z - v\left(\sigma_x + \sigma_y\right)$$

$$\sigma_z = E\varepsilon_z + v\left(\sigma_x + \sigma_y\right)$$

$$= 0 \text{ MPa} + 0.3\left(-90 + 30\right) \text{ MPa}$$

$$= -18 \text{ MPa}$$

Then ε_x and ε_y can be obtained directly from Equations (2.6) and (2.7):

$$\varepsilon_x = \frac{\sigma_x}{E} - \frac{v}{E}\left(\sigma_y + \sigma_z\right)$$

$$= \frac{-90 \times 10^6}{210 \times 10^9} - \frac{0.3}{210 \times 10^9}\left(30 - 18\right) \times 10^6$$

$$= -4.5 \times 10^{-4}$$

$$\varepsilon_y = \frac{\sigma_y}{E} - \frac{v}{E}\left(\sigma_x + \sigma_z\right)$$

$$= \frac{30 \times 10^6}{210 \times 10^9} - \frac{0.3}{210 \times 10^9}\left(-90 - 18\right) \times 10^6$$

$$= 3.0 \times 10^{-4}$$

SAQ 2.7 (Learning outcomes 2.1, 2.3 and 2.4)

The two-dimensional state of stress at a point in the concrete lining of a railway tunnel is shown in Figure 2.18. Assuming plane strain, determine all components of the three-dimensional strain tensor at this point. (Take $E = 19$ GPa and $v = 0.2$ for concrete.)

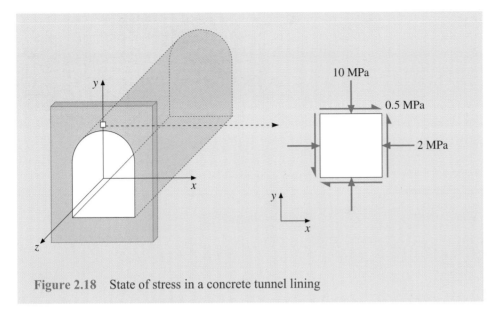

Figure 2.18 State of stress in a concrete tunnel lining

As I've said before, it is often the principal stresses that are of most interest when considering the structural integrity of a component, since these have the greatest magnitude. Constitutive Equations (2.6)–(2.8) apply whether or not σ_x, σ_y and σ_z are principal stresses, since shear stresses do not contribute to the direct strains, provided the shear deformations are small. But in the special case where there are no shear stresses, σ_x, σ_y and σ_z are identical to the principal stresses σ_1, σ_2 and σ_3 and the constitutive equations simply become:

$$\varepsilon_1 = \frac{\sigma_1}{E} - \frac{v}{E}(\sigma_2 + \sigma_3) \tag{2.11}$$

$$\varepsilon_2 = \frac{\sigma_2}{E} - \frac{v}{E}(\sigma_1 + \sigma_3) \tag{2.12}$$

$$\varepsilon_3 = \frac{\sigma_3}{E} - \frac{v}{E}(\sigma_1 + \sigma_2) \tag{2.13}$$

where ε_1, ε_2 and ε_3 are the *principal strains* that occur in the same directions as the principal stresses.

Equations (2.11)–(2.13) can also be combined and rearranged so that the principal stresses are written in terms of the principal strains:

$$\sigma_1 = \frac{E}{(1+v)(1-2v)}\left[(1-v)\varepsilon_1 + v\varepsilon_2 + v\varepsilon_3\right] \tag{2.14}$$

$$\sigma_2 = \frac{E}{(1+v)(1-2v)}\left[v\varepsilon_1 + (1-v)\varepsilon_2 + v\varepsilon_3\right] \tag{2.15}$$

$$\sigma_3 = \frac{E}{(1+v)(1-2v)}\left[v\varepsilon_1 + v\varepsilon_2 + (1-v)\varepsilon_3\right] \tag{2.16}$$

Again, Equations (2.14)–(2.16) can also be used to obtain identical expressions for non-principal stresses and strains just by replacing the suffixes 1, 2 and 3 with x, y and z respectively.

If shear strains are large, then the angular distortions are large and the infinitesimal element, which defines the 'strain at a point' that we are seeking, no longer has parallel sides. Hence the analysis breaks down.

In practice, states of deformation are often plane stress or plane strain, in which case the equations are made simpler by inserting $\sigma_3 = 0$ for plane stress and $\varepsilon_3 = 0$ for plane strain. This allows Equations (2.11)–(2.16) to be rewritten as in Table 2.4. To tackle a two-dimensional problem you can use either the plane stress or plane strain equations in this table, or apply the full three-dimensional equations. Either way, don't be put off by this list of equations: *you don't need to remember them, but you do need to be able to use them.* As an engineer or designer carrying out stress analysis you might want to think of them as the tools of your trade.

Table 2.4   The two-dimensional elastic constitutive equations for plane stress and plane strain

Plane stress	Plane strain
$\varepsilon_1 = \dfrac{1}{E}\left(\sigma_1 - v\sigma_2\right)$	$\varepsilon_1 = \dfrac{1+v}{E}\left[(1-v)\sigma_1 - v\sigma_2\right]$
$\varepsilon_2 = \dfrac{1}{E}\left(\sigma_2 - v\sigma_1\right)$	$\varepsilon_2 = \dfrac{1+v}{E}\left[(1-v)\sigma_2 - v\sigma_1\right]$
$\varepsilon_3 = \dfrac{-v}{E}\left(\sigma_1 + \sigma_2\right)$	$\varepsilon_3 = 0$
$\sigma_1 = \dfrac{E}{1-v^2}\left(\varepsilon_1 + v\varepsilon_2\right)$	$\sigma_1 = \dfrac{E}{(1+v)(1-2v)}\left[(1-v)\varepsilon_1 + v\varepsilon_2\right]$
$\sigma_2 = \dfrac{E}{1-v^2}\left(\varepsilon_2 + v\varepsilon_1\right)$	$\sigma_2 = \dfrac{E}{(1+v)(1-2v)}\left[v\varepsilon_1 + (1-v)\varepsilon_2\right]$
$\sigma_3 = 0$	$\sigma_3 = \dfrac{Ev}{(1+v)(1-2v)}\left(\varepsilon_1 + \varepsilon_2\right)$

SAQ 2.8 (Learning outcomes 2.1, 2.4 and 2.6)

In Block 1 Part 1 you determined the principal stresses at the surface of a piece of pressurized pipework that was being gripped and twisted by a wrench, as shown in Figure 2.19, assuming plane stress. If the pipework is made of steel ($E = 210$ GPa, $v = 0.3$), what are the corresponding principal strains for this stress state?

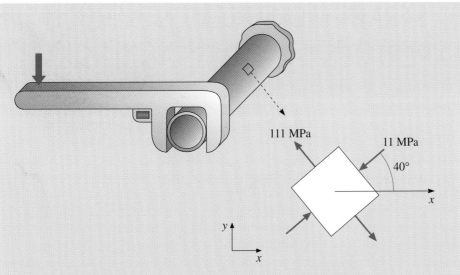

Figure 2.19 Principal stresses at the surface of a pressurized pipe

SAQ 2.9 (Learning outcomes 2.1, 2.3 and 2.6)

In an experiment to determine the stresses in a welded aluminium plate, the following strains are measured at a point:

$\varepsilon_x = 3200 \times 10^{-6}$

$\varepsilon_y = -450 \times 10^{-6}$

$\varepsilon_z = -920 \times 10^{-6}$.

It is assumed that the measurement directions are the principal strain directions. The elastic constants for the aluminium alloy used are $E = 70$ GPa and $v = 0.3$.

(In this case you cannot assume either plane stress or plane strain.)

(a) Write the strain tensor for this measurement point.

(b) Calculate the principal stresses at this point, and write the stress tensor.

There is an important message to be learned from the answer to SAQ 2.9: because of the Poisson's ratio effect, measuring a compressive strain in a particular direction does not mean that there will be an associated compressive stress. It's very important not to think that you can use the uniaxial approximation of $\sigma = E\varepsilon$ as a 'rule of thumb' to estimate stresses from strains in two-dimensional or three-dimensional situations.

6 STRAIN MEASUREMENT: EXPERIMENTAL STRESS ANALYSIS

The preceding sections have treated the analysis of stress and strain as a largely mathematical problem, to be solved using appropriate equations or graphical analysis. You have seen that even experimentally determined material properties are generalized into constitutive equations that allow the engineer to convert between stress and strain. But it is never a good idea to rely entirely on theoretical predictions. Under certain circumstances it is essential to obtain a direct measure of the quantities in which we are interested, e.g. when analysing a component of complex geometry, when the precise nature of loading is unknown or difficult to characterize, or simply to check important calculations on which people's lives may depend. If you were an engineer responsible for the structural integrity of a new aircraft wing, for instance, then you would want to make pretty sure that you had got things right before take-off.

So what should we try to measure: stress or strain? Well, there is usually a need to characterize the performance of components in terms of their load-bearing capacity. This in turn leads to the specification of component performance in terms of acceptable, i.e. safe, levels of stress. But if you think about it, a force does not usually manifest itself within a material except by the deformation with which it is associated. In other words, stresses cannot be measured directly: they have to be determined from displacements and strains, using the appropriate stress–strain relations for the material.

Here I will introduce you to two common, highly contrasting, methods of experimental stress analysis. First, we will look at *photoelasticity*, a useful 'full field' method for measuring the stress state over relatively large areas of a structure. Then we will move on to a detailed examination of the use of electrical resistance *strain gauges* for localized 'point' strain measurement, including the analysis and interpretation of measurements using strain transformation equations and Mohr's circle.

6.1 Photoelasticity

Photoelasticity is an experimental method that makes use of an optical effect that occurs in some transparent materials, such as glass, epoxy and polycarbonate. Under certain circumstances the stress in these materials is associated with the appearance of visible patterns. For example, you may have seen some of these when looking at light reflected off a toughened car window (Figure 2.20).

For the purposes of experimental stress analysis, a specific optical arrangement is used. Take a look at Figure 2.21, which shows the optical pattern visible within a circular disc of epoxy resin that is in compression across its vertical diameter. The disc has been illuminated from behind with a beam of monochromatic light (that is, light of a single wavelength or colour) and is viewed between two sheets of polarizing material (like that used in sunglasses), as shown in Figure 2.22. Under these conditions the monochromatic polarized light wave that passes through the

Figure 2.20 The photoelastic effect in a car window, as you would see it wearing Polaroid® sunglasses. The effect is associated with the internal stresses created during manufacture of the toughened glass

stressed disc is split into two separate rays. These two waves travel at different speeds and can interfere with each other, causing reduction or reinforcement of the visible light intensity and the formation of light and dark 'fringes', depending upon the local stress in the material. Knowing the full physics of this process is not necessary for the purposes of understanding how photoelasticity can be applied to engineering stress analysis. However, you do need to know that each dark fringe has a simple, important significance: *it is a contour line joining together points in the disc with the same value of principal stress difference* $(\sigma_1 - \sigma_2)$ *in a plane perpendicular to the light beam.*

A material in which light rays split into two in this way is said to be *birefringent*.

Figure 2.21 Isochromatic fringes in a disc of uniform thickness compressed across its vertical diameter

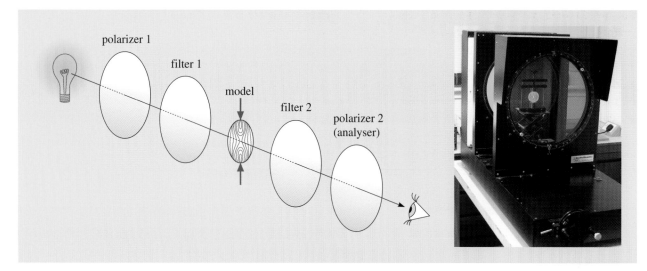

Figure 2.22   Optical arrangement for viewing isochromatic photoelastic fringes. Note that the set-up also includes special optical filters (called quarter-wave plates) for correct polarization of the light

In other words, all points on a dark fringe have the same value of $(\sigma_1 - \sigma_2)$. Each dark fringe is said to have a *fringe order N*, where N is a whole number from zero upwards. For the purposes of engineering stress analysis there is a simple relationship between the principal stress difference and the fringe order in a stressed photoelastic material:

$$\sigma_1 - \sigma_2 = \frac{Nf}{t}$$

where f is a constant for a given material, known as the *material fringe constant*, and t is the thickness of the material. By observing a pattern of fringes and assigning an order N to each dark fringe, the principal stress difference can be mapped. Note that the principal stress difference is an important quantity because it is directly related to the maximum shear stress – see ▽ **Relationship between $\tau_{\max}$ and $(\sigma_1 - \sigma_2)$** ▽.

▽ Relationship between $\tau_{\max}$ and $(\sigma_1 - \sigma_2)$

Recall (from Block 1 Part 1, Section 6) that the maximum shear stress in a plane element subjected to stresses σ_x, σ_y and τ_{xy} is given by:

$$\tau_{\max} = \pm\sqrt{\left(\frac{\sigma_x - \sigma_y}{2}\right)^2 + \tau_{xy}^2}$$

When σ_x and σ_y lie along the principal stress directions, the shear stress vanishes ($\tau_{xy} = 0$) and the normal stresses become principal stresses ($\sigma_x = \sigma_1$, $\sigma_y = \sigma_2$).

So we can write in that case:

$$\tau_{\max} = \pm\sqrt{\left(\frac{\sigma_1 - \sigma_2}{2}\right)^2 + 0}$$

That is:

$$\tau_{\max} = \frac{\sigma_1 - \sigma_2}{2}$$

In other words, the maximum shear stress in a plane is equal to half the magnitude of the principal stress difference $(\sigma_1 - \sigma_2)$ in that plane.

△

But how do we know what value of N to assign to each fringe in the disc of Figure 2.21, for example? Well, this can really only be done by applying load to the disc gradually. With no applied load the disc would appear completely black – there is zero stress everywhere and so the disc is covered in a single dark fringe of order 'zero'. Gradual loading causes that black area to shrink and a new black fringe to appear, of order 1. Further loading sees new fringes come into view of order 2, then order 3 and so on. At high loads some of the lower-order fringes might disappear. Thankfully, in this case the experimentalist kept track of which fringe was which as the disc was being loaded. In Figure 2.21, the extreme left-hand and right-hand fringes are first-order fringes and neighbouring fringes differ in order by one. This means that the two central fringes are of order 4 (in fact, although it is not clear, these are part of the same loop). At the top and bottom there are further loops, with orders from $N = 5$ to $N = 27$.

The 'Photoelasticity' programme on the DVD shows how photoelastic measurements are made.

EXERCISE 2.6

Estimate the approximate value of the maximum principal stress difference in the epoxy disc, thickness 5 mm, shown in Figure 2.21. Assume the fringe constant for epoxy is 9.5 kN m^{-1}.

Clearly, most engineering structural components are not actually made of photoelastic materials. Instead, photoelastic studies are often carried out on scale models of real structures. In such cases it is assumed that the *distribution* of stress in the smaller model is the same as that in the larger component, even though the stress magnitudes might be different. See, for example, the model of a jet-engine turbine in Figure 2.23.

To give you an idea about how this works, I will go back to the simple hook design we explored in Block 1 Part 1.

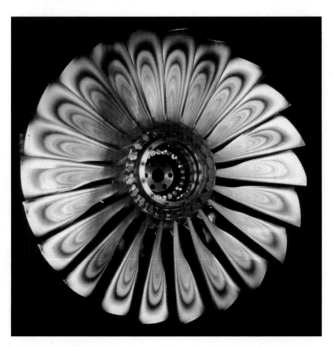

Figure 2.23 Photoelastic model of a jet-engine turbine array. The array is running at a fast rotation, and a high-speed photograph has been taken, revealing the fringe pattern in the blades

SAQ 2.10 (Learning outcomes 2.1 and 2.7)

Figure 2.24 shows a photoelastic model of a hook made from 6 mm thick epoxy, identical in shape to the hook that you examined in Block 1 Part 1, but larger in scale (all the dimensions of the epoxy hook are 1.5 times bigger, in fact). The epoxy hook has been illuminated using monochromatic polarized light and loaded using circular rollers, which you should just be able to make out in the image. The vertical black lines that cut across the top and bottom of the hook are (opaque) wires through which a tensile force of 120 N was applied.

(a) Ignore the fringes for a moment. Calculate the average stress expected across the straight neck of the hook where it has a uniform width of 15 mm. Assuming this stress is *uniaxial*, deduce the magnitude of $(\sigma_1 - \sigma_2)$ in the neck.

(b) Now concentrate on the fringe pattern across the centre of the hook as highlighted in the exploded view presented in Figure 2.24. The zero-order dark fringe is marked in the figure; the fringe loop surrounding this corresponds to $N = 1$ and so on.

   (i) By counting the fringes to the right of the zero-order fringe, estimate the principal stress difference $(\sigma_1 - \sigma_2)$ at the right-hand edge of the hook. Assume the fringe constant for epoxy is 9.5 kN m^{-1}.

   (ii) In the same way, estimate $(\sigma_1 - \sigma_2)$ at the left-hand edge of the hook.

(c) By what ratio has the principal stress difference $(\sigma_1 - \sigma_2)$ in the neck been magnified at the inner and outer edges of the curved part of the epoxy hook?

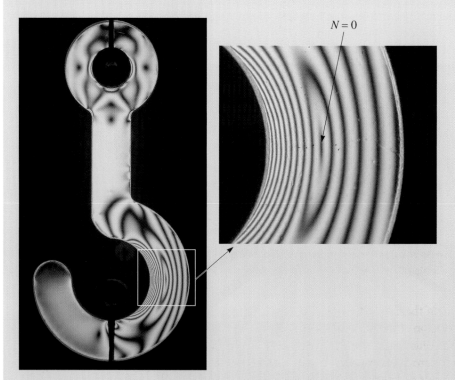

Figure 2.24   Isochromatic fringes in a photoelastic model of a simple hook design

SAQ 2.11 (Learning outcomes 2.1, 2.3 and 2.7)

Figure 2.25 shows the finite element mesh that we also examined during our earlier analysis of the hook geometry. This time, however, I have superimposed values of principal stress difference on the mesh, as calculated by the finite element code. Recall that in the finite element model a 500 N load was applied, leading to a uniaxial stress of 50 MPa in the hook neck. We could not apply such a large tensile load to the epoxy hook because it would break; the finite element model assumed that the hook was made of steel.

By what ratio has $(\sigma_1 - \sigma_2)$ in the neck been magnified at the inner and outer edges of the curved part of the steel hook, as modelled by the finite element analysis?

Compare these with the ratios you calculated for the epoxy hook in SAQ 2.10. What do you conclude?

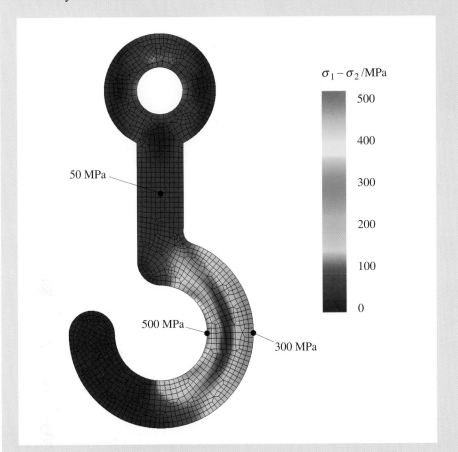

Figure 2.25 Principal stress difference predicted by finite element analysis of a simple hook design

One of the difficulties you may have noticed in tackling SAQ 2.11 concerns the precision of the measurements that can be made by looking at monochromatic photoelastic images. For example, the inner edge of the curved part of the hook in Figure 2.24 doesn't seem to coincide exactly with a dark fringe, so it's a little difficult to determine the stress with certainty. There are special calibration procedures for improving accuracy of measurements with monochromatic light, but

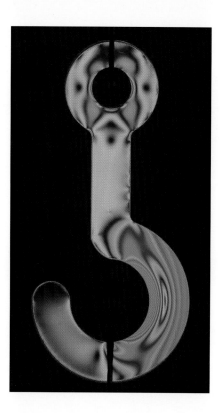

Figure 2.26 Polychromatic fringes in a photoelastic model of a simple hook design

another approach involves the use of polychromatic 'white' light (that is, light that contains many wave frequencies, and hence colours). In this case the optical pattern for the epoxy hook appears as shown in Figure 2.26, with black and white fringes replaced by a repeating spectrum of colours. The positions of these colours provide the experimentalist with more precise information about the stress state at any point in the photoelastic model.

Figure 2.24 and Figure 2.26 are examples of two-dimensional *photoelasticity*, in which analysis is limited to the investigation of the stress distribution in two-dimensional models of uniform thickness loaded in plane stress and viewed in light that is transmitted *through* the material. An alternative is to use a sheet of photoelastic material as a type of coating, bonded directly to the surface of a structure using a reflective cement. Strains in the structure are transferred to the coating, causing a fringe pattern to appear when it is illuminated with polarized light. Curved surfaces may be coated, allowing the method to be used on almost any type of structure.

6.2 The electrical resistance strain gauge

Essentially, a strain gauge is an electrical conductor that is bonded to the surface of a workpiece. If the workpiece is deformed, the resistance of the conductor changes; by measuring this change, the strain in the workpiece can be deduced. You probably know that the resistance R to current flow in a piece of wire depends on geometric factors, length L and cross-sectional area A, and also on the material from which the wire is made, through its resistivity ρ:

$$R = \frac{\rho L}{A}$$

This simple relationship provides the important link between dimensional changes and resistance.

EXERCISE 2.7

Consider the Poisson effect in a wire that is strained from an initial length, L to $L + \Delta L$. What overall effect will the change in dimensions have on the wire's resistance?

For elastic deformation of a wire, the change in area A depends on the change in length L, because of the Poisson effect. In practice it is found that the proportional change in resistance $\Delta R/R$ simply depends on the proportional change in length $\Delta L/L$ (i.e. the direct strain ε) of the wire:

$$\frac{\Delta R}{R} = K\frac{\Delta L}{L} = K\varepsilon \tag{2.17}$$

where K is called the *sensitivity factor*, or *gauge factor*, and contains the effect of any change in resistivity and of the Poisson's ratio of the material. As it turns out, provided the temperature doesn't change too much, there is an approximately linear relationship between $\Delta R/R$ and $\Delta L/L$; in other words, K can be considered as a constant.

Hence, if we can measure the change in resistance to a good enough accuracy, using a material of known K and R, then we should have an accurate measure of the strain that caused the change. Elastic deformations in a safely stressed engineering component might easily reach several hundred microstrain, so it makes sense to be able to distinguish between variations at least two orders of magnitude smaller than this, say $5\mu\varepsilon$. What kind of resistance change might this cause in a typical metal?

EXERCISE 2.8

Imagine that you are considering the idea of using a small piece of copper wire, 5 mm long by 0.5 mm diameter, as a strain gauge. What change in resistance will be associated with a small elastic longitudinal strain of 5×10^{-6} in this material?

(Assume $\rho = 0.017 \times 10^{-6}$ Ω m and $K = 2$ for copper.)

EXERCISE 2.9

The resistance change you will have calculated in Exercise 2.8 is very small and difficult to measure. What properties would you look for in a wire strain gauge that might make measurement of small strains easier?

Given that elastic strain in a wire is likely to give rise to only very small changes in resistance, there is a requirement to make R large in order to make ΔR easy to

Figure 2.27   A wire strain gauge

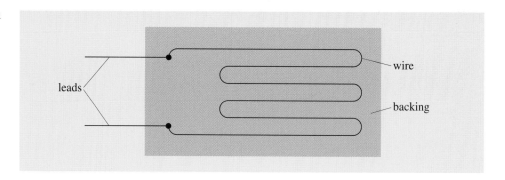

measure. This has two geometrical implications: a small cross section and a long wire length are beneficial, but we need to consider these factors a little more carefully. In the case of a small cross section, a very thin wire has the added benefit that it will not noticeably reinforce the component to which it is attached – which is clearly a good thing. On the other hand, the use of a very long wire is potentially problematic. In general, the strain that we are likely to want to measure will vary over the surface of a component, and in fact we are most likely to be interested in areas where the strain gradient is steepest. A long wire bonded to the surface would read the average strain over the length to which it is fixed and might not reflect accurately the value of the maximum strain or its position. To discriminate small areas of high strain then, a short wire is needed, whereas a long wire is required to make the resistance large. The compromise solution is to fold the wire, as shown in Figure 2.27, so that a long wire can occupy a small area. Put it onto a backing to make it easy to handle and it becomes a strain gauge. The wire is made from an alloy that has a high resistivity, the most common materials being Constantin and Karma (see Table 2.5). Gauges are sold in a wide range of lengths from about 0.2 mm upwards.

Table 2.5   Resistivity table

Material		Resistivity/$\mu\Omega$ m
Copper	(Cu)	0.017
Iron	(Fe)	0.100
Nickel	(Ni)	0.078
'Constantin'	(Ni/Cu alloy)	0.490
'Karma'	(Ni/Cr/Fe/Cu alloy)	1.300

One problem is the existence of U-bends in the wire, which have some length in the lateral direction and will, therefore, register a change in resistance as a function of lateral strain. This effect will change the value of the sensitivity factor K from that of a straight wire. We can get round this difficulty easily by using the value of K for the particular gauge in question, the *gauge factor*. Manufacturers calibrate gauges by measuring their response to known uniaxial deformations and quote values of K to purchasers of the gauges. Most gauges have a K value of approximately 2.

A final, significant improvement to the design we have considered so far, commonly adopted by manufacturers of small modern gauges, is to make the gauge from etched foil about 2–10 μm thick (Figure 2.28). This has the effect of improving heat dissipation, as the foil has a larger surface-to-volume ratio than wire. It is important

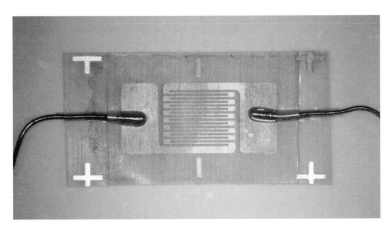

Figure 2.28   A foil strain gauge

to minimize any heating effects, as a change in temperature of the gauge will affect both the resistivity of the material and its dimensions.

6.3 Strain transformation

Now, put yourself in the position of an experimentalist with a cabinet full of strain gauges and a workpiece. Where do you put your strain gauge and in what direction do you align it? In general, the choice of gauge location depends on what you want to know, and it usually requires an educated judgement as to where the strains might be large. For complex structures it may be necessary to place gauges in several places: when NASA tested new 'forward swept' wings for their X-29 demonstration aircraft (Figure 2.29), several thousand sensors were used to measure pressure, loads and deflection while the aircraft manoeuvred at different speeds. On the other hand, you will probably have less money than NASA, so it makes sense to exercise a little discretion.

So what should the orientation of a gauge be in order to detect the largest strain? If your workpiece were a simple beam under uniaxial loading then the answer would be obvious, because the maximum strains occur on the long axis of the beam. In general, however, you would not be sticking gauges on such simple structures and you would not know the direction of maximum strain. In such cases it is beneficial to attach *three* gauges close together, each aligned along arbitrary, convenient

Figure 2.29   NASA's X-29 experimental plane designed to test new concepts in aerodynamics

axes. The problem then becomes one of determining the magnitude and direction of the maximum strain from these gauge readings, as none of the gauges may line up with the direction where the strain is a maximum. Nonetheless, it is possible to calculate the maximum strain from three such gauges, and to do this we need *strain transformation equations*, in the same way that stress transformation equations were required to find the direction of maximum stresses at a particular point.

The strain transformation equations can be derived directly from definitions of strain; they are purely geometrical relationships and do not require a knowledge of material properties. Derivations are commonly available in 'mechanics of materials' textbooks should you require them; for the purposes of carrying out engineering analyses I will simply quote them, drawing on an analogy with the stress transformation equations. As usual, you will not be expected to remember these equations, but you will be required to use them. Just as for stress, the two-dimensional strain transformation equations describe the normal and shear strain components, ε_θ and γ_θ, in a direction rotated anticlockwise by an angle θ from the x-axis of an *xy*-coordinate system:

$$\varepsilon_\theta = \frac{1}{2}\left(\varepsilon_x + \varepsilon_y\right) + \frac{1}{2}\left(\varepsilon_x - \varepsilon_y\right)\cos 2\theta + \frac{\gamma_{xy}}{2}\sin 2\theta \tag{2.18}$$

$$\frac{\gamma_\theta}{2} = -\frac{1}{2}\left(\varepsilon_x - \varepsilon_y\right)\sin 2\theta + \frac{\gamma_{xy}}{2}\cos 2\theta \tag{2.19}$$

If you compare these with the stress transformation equations from Block 1 Part 1 you will see that the form is exactly the same, with τ_{xy} equivalent to $\gamma_{xy}/2$ and τ_θ equivalent to $\gamma_\theta/2$.

The really useful thing about the transformation equations is that they allow us to calculate the angle at which the maximum stresses and strains occur. Remember, it is these extreme values that are most likely to have implications for the integrity of a component. For strain, just as for stress, there are orientations of an element for which shear strains vanish and the normal strains attain maximum and minimum values, called *principal strains*. For an isotropic material, the directions of the principal strains (the principal axes) are the same as the principal stress directions.

I will pursue this analogy between stress and strain by telling you that it is possible to derive a full set of equations describing principal strains and maximum shear strains, along with their respective orientations, that are directly equivalent to the expressions for stress that we looked at in Block 1 Part 1. For simplicity, I've laid out all these equations in Table 2.6.

Finally, I would just like to remind you that, for surface strain measurements, the 'free surface' condition applies (surface normal stress $\sigma_z = 0$) and a state of plane stress exists. But, if you look at Equations (2.18) and (2.19) you might think that they are for plane strain conditions only, since they don't include any z-axis strain components, ε_z, γ_{xz} or γ_{yz}. However, because of the Poisson effect, there will be a strain ε_z normal to the surface, but a surface strain gauge is oriented such that it can't detect strains in that direction, and hence Equations (2.18) and (2.19) are applicable. In fact, the normal to a free surface is a principal axis of strain.

Try *Mechanics of Materials* by R. C. Hibbeler (published by Pearson Prentice Hall) or *Mechanics of Materials* by F. P. Beer, E. R. Johnston and J. T. DeWolf (McGraw Hill).

Table 2.6   The two-dimensional stress and strain equations

Stress	Strain
Stress transformations	Strain transformations
$\sigma_\theta = \frac{1}{2}\left(\sigma_x + \sigma_y\right) + \frac{1}{2}\left(\sigma_x - \sigma_y\right)\cos 2\theta + \tau_{xy}\sin 2\theta$	$\varepsilon_\theta = \frac{1}{2}\left(\varepsilon_x + \varepsilon_y\right) + \frac{1}{2}\left(\varepsilon_x - \varepsilon_y\right)\cos 2\theta + \frac{\gamma_{xy}}{2}\sin 2\theta$
$\tau_\theta = -\frac{1}{2}\left(\sigma_x - \sigma_y\right)\sin 2\theta + \tau_{xy}\cos 2\theta$	$\frac{\gamma_\theta}{2} = -\frac{1}{2}\left(\varepsilon_x - \varepsilon_y\right)\sin 2\theta + \frac{\gamma_{xy}}{2}\cos 2\theta$
Principal stresses	Principal strains
$\sigma_{1,2} = \frac{\sigma_x + \sigma_y}{2} \pm \sqrt{\left(\frac{\sigma_x - \sigma_y}{2}\right)^2 + \tau_{xy}^2}$	$\varepsilon_{1,2} = \frac{\varepsilon_x + \varepsilon_y}{2} \pm \sqrt{\left(\frac{\varepsilon_x - \varepsilon_y}{2}\right)^2 + \left(\frac{\gamma_{xy}}{2}\right)^2}$
Principal stress directions	Principal strain directions
$\tan 2\theta_p = \frac{2\tau_{xy}}{\sigma_x - \sigma_y}$	$\tan 2\theta_p = \frac{\gamma_{xy}}{\varepsilon_x - \varepsilon_y}$
Maximum shear stresses	Maximum shear strains
$\tau_{max} = \pm\sqrt{\left(\frac{\sigma_x - \sigma_y}{2}\right)^2 + \tau_{xy}^2}$	$\frac{\gamma_{max}}{2} = \pm\sqrt{\left(\frac{\varepsilon_x - \varepsilon_y}{2}\right)^2 + \left(\frac{\gamma_{xy}}{2}\right)^2}$
Maximum shear stress directions	Maximum shear strain directions
$\tan 2\theta_s = -\frac{\sigma_x - \sigma_y}{2\tau_{xy}}$	$\tan 2\theta_s = -\frac{\varepsilon_x - \varepsilon_y}{\gamma_{xy}}$

6.4 Mohr's strain circle

Rather than directly applying the equations of Table 2.6 to determine the state of strain at a point, it is possible, if you prefer, to construct a Mohr's circle for strain in the same general way as you would construct a Mohr's stress circle. The main things to take into account are as follows:

- Although ε_θ replaces σ_θ for the horizontal axis in the strain circle, the vertical axis represents $\gamma_\theta/2$, since this is equivalent to τ.

- The centre coordinates of the strain circle are $(\frac{1}{2}(\varepsilon_x + \varepsilon_y), 0)$, compared with $(\frac{1}{2}(\sigma_x + \sigma_y), 0)$ for the stress circle.

- The radius of the strain circle is given by the maximum shear strain rather than the maximum shear stress.

The simplest way to see how the strain circle works is to go through the following worked example.

EXAMPLE

At a point in a structure the strains are $\varepsilon_x = 9 \times 10^{-4}$, $\varepsilon_y = 1 \times 10^{-4}$ and $\gamma_{xy} = -8 \times 10^{-4}$. Use Mohr's strain circle to find the values of the principal strains, the maximum shear strain and their respective orientations.

SOLUTION

In a similar fashion to the stress circle, points at opposite ends of a diameter are plotted to construct the strain circle. Remember, however, that the vertical axis refers to *half* the shear strain. The steps are:

1   Draw axes for the direct strain ε_θ and the shear strain $\gamma_\theta/2$. ε_θ should be positive to the *right* of the origin and $\gamma_\theta/2$ positive *below* the origin.

2   Plot the points $(\varepsilon_x, \gamma_{xy}/2)$ and $(\varepsilon_y, -\gamma_{xy}/2)$.

3   Join these points using a straight line that should intercept the horizontal axis at $\varepsilon_\theta = \frac{1}{2}(\varepsilon_x + \varepsilon_y)$.

4   Construct a circle with this line as a diameter.

For the given strains, Mohr's circle is shown in Figure 2.30 with points $(\varepsilon_x, \gamma_{xy}/2)$ and $(\varepsilon_y, -\gamma_{xy}/2)$ joined to form diameter XY. Recall that these points represent the shear and normal strains on planes perpendicular to the x- and y-directions respectively.

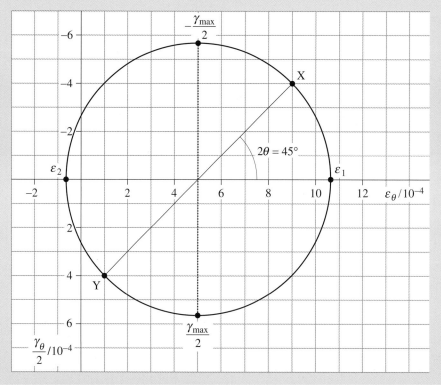

Figure 2.30   Mohr's circle of strain

The principal strains ε_1 and ε_2 are estimated from the points at which the circle intercepts the horizontal axis, where shear strains are zero. From Figure 2.30, $\varepsilon_1 \approx 10.7 \times 10^{-4}$ and $\varepsilon_2 \approx -0.7 \times 10^{-4}$.

As with the stress circle, a rotation of θ in the material is represented by 2θ on the diagram. The direction of the maximum principal strain ε_1 is $45°/2 = 22.5°$ *clockwise* from the x-direction, point X in Figure 2.30. The minimum principal strain ε_2 is oriented $135°/2 = 67.5°$ *anticlockwise* from the x-direction.

The maximum shear strains are determined from the upper and lower extremities of the circle, $\gamma_{max}/2 \approx \pm5.6 \times 10^{-4}$; hence $\gamma_{max} \approx \pm11.2 \times 10^{-4}$. These occur on planes oriented $22.5°$ *anticlockwise* with respect to the xy-coordinate system.

EXERCISE 2.10

Check the results of the above worked example by using the equations of Table 2.6 directly.

SAQ 2.12 (Learning outcomes 2.1 and 2.5)

What are the principal strains, and in which direction do they occur, when the strains at a point are given by $\varepsilon_x = 7 \times 10^{-4}$, $\varepsilon_y = -5 \times 10^{-4}$ and $\gamma_{xy} = 8 \times 10^{-4}$? Produce either an algebraic solution using the equations in Table 2.6 or a graphical solution using Mohr's circle, whichever you find easier.

6.5 Rosette strain gauge analysis

Although Mohr's strain circle is useful for estimating and visualizing the state of strain at a point, we can't apply it, without modification, to analysing data from surface strain gauges. The problem is that strain gauges don't measure shear deformation, only linear extensions and contractions. So how do we determine the full state of strain using gauges that can read only direct strain?

If I fix a single strain gauge to my component at a certain angle θ to whatever I choose as the x-axis direction, then the gauge tells me the strain ε_θ in that direction. Now, I want to make use of the strain transformation equation, $\varepsilon_\theta = \frac{1}{2}(\varepsilon_x + \varepsilon_y) + \frac{1}{2}(\varepsilon_x - \varepsilon_y)\cos 2\theta + (\gamma_{xy}/2)\sin 2\theta$, but there are three unknowns that I need to find: ε_x, ε_y and γ_{xy}. So the thing to do is to take *three* measurements of ε_θ, each at a different angle θ. This will give me three sets of equations that I can then solve simultaneously to find the three unknowns. In practice, the best thing to do is to arrange the gauges around a point and take all the readings at once. Such an arrangement is made possible by a *strain gauge rosette*, which consists of three interconnected gauges on a single backing. It is sensible to choose the directions of the gauges so that the resulting sums are made simple, and this has led to two common types of arrangement: the 45° and 60° rosettes (Figure 2.31).

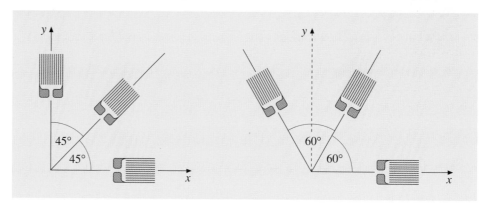

Figure 2.31   Two patterns of rosette strain gauge

There are special constructions for drawing a Mohr's circle directly from three strain gauge readings. It is not, however, worth the potential confusion of learning more rules for a graphical construction, as the equations are relatively simple to use.

The easiest way to deal with these two rosette configurations is to align one of the gauges along the arbitrary x-axis, as shown in Figure 2.31. Once ε_x, ε_y and γ_{xy} have been determined the principal strains, for example, can then be deduced either graphically or algebraically, as usual. I will deal with the technique by showing you a couple of examples, starting with the 45° rosette. This is the easiest arrangement to analyse; because of the way the gauges are aligned, both ε_x and ε_y are known straight away.

EXAMPLE

A 45° strain gauge rosette gives the readings shown in Figure 2.32. Find the strains ε_x, ε_y and γ_{xy}.

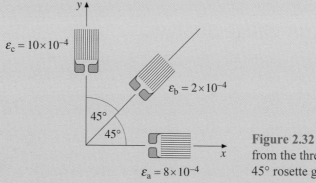

Figure 2.32   Direct strains from the three elements of a 45° rosette gauge

SOLUTION

Referring to Figure 2.32, ε_x and ε_y can be deduced directly:

$$\varepsilon_x = \varepsilon_a = 8 \times 10^{-4}$$
$$\varepsilon_y = \varepsilon_c = 10 \times 10^{-4}$$

Also, at $\theta = 45°$ we have $\varepsilon_\theta = \varepsilon_b = 2 \times 10^{-4}$. So we can use this as a known value of ε_θ at a known angle.

All these values can be substituted into the transformation equation to determine γ_{xy}:

$$\varepsilon_\theta = \frac{1}{2}\left(\varepsilon_x + \varepsilon_y\right) + \frac{1}{2}\left(\varepsilon_x - \varepsilon_y\right)\cos 2\theta + \frac{\gamma_{xy}}{2}\sin 2\theta$$

$$2\times 10^{-4} = \frac{1}{2}(8+10)10^{-4} + 0 + \left(\frac{\gamma_{xy}}{2}\times 1\right)$$

$$\gamma_{xy} = -14\times 10^{-4}$$

So the state of strain has been found from the gauge readings to be $\varepsilon_x = 8 \times 10^{-4}$, $\varepsilon_y = 10 \times 10^{-4}$ and $\gamma_{xy} = -14 \times 10^{-4}$.

The reasons for the widespread use of two types of strain rosette are largely historical. Although the computation associated with the 45° arrangement is quite straightforward, the analysis associated with the 60° arrangement, as you will see in the following example, is a little lengthier, but such considerations are a throwback to the days before electronic calculators and computers. It is often presumed that the wider angular spread between gauges in the 60° rosette gives a better reflection of the underlying stress state in the material; such an arrangement also means that the gauges are very slightly more sensitive to small changes in strain. However, for most practical purposes, the difference is negligible. The choice usually comes down to minor practical concerns, such as the available space on the component surface, solder tab arrangements, or quite simply availability of gauges from the stockist.

EXAMPLE

A 60° strain gauge rosette gives the readings shown in Figure 2.33. Find the strains ε_x, ε_y and γ_{xy}.

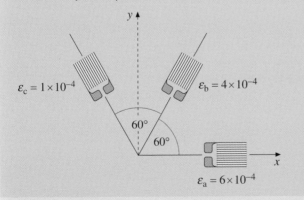

Figure 2.33 Direct strains from the elements of a 60° rosette gauge

SOLUTION

From Figure 2.33, ε_x is equivalent to ε_a:

$$\varepsilon_x = \varepsilon_a = 6\times 10^{-4}$$

Also, $\varepsilon_b = 4 \times 10^{-4}$ at $\theta = 60°$ and $\varepsilon_c = 1 \times 10^{-4}$ at $\theta = 120°$. Substituting these into the transformation equation:

$$\varepsilon_\theta = \frac{1}{2}\left(\varepsilon_x + \varepsilon_y\right) + \frac{1}{2}\left(\varepsilon_x - \varepsilon_y\right)\cos 2\theta + \frac{\gamma_{xy}}{2}\sin 2\theta$$

gives, at $\theta = 60°$, $\varepsilon_\theta = \varepsilon_b$:

$$4\times10^{-4} = \frac{1}{2}\left(\varepsilon_x + \varepsilon_y\right) + \frac{1}{2}\left(\varepsilon_x - \varepsilon_y\right)(-0.5) + \frac{\gamma_{xy}}{2}(0.87) \qquad (2.20)$$

and at $\theta = 120°$, $\varepsilon_\theta = \varepsilon_c$:

$$1\times10^{-4} = \frac{1}{2}\left(\varepsilon_x + \varepsilon_y\right) + \frac{1}{2}\left(\varepsilon_x - \varepsilon_y\right)(-0.5) + \frac{\gamma_{xy}}{2}(-0.87) \qquad (2.21)$$

Subtracting Equation (2.21) from Equation (2.20) gives:

$$3\times10^{-4} = 0.87\gamma_{xy}$$

$$\gamma_{xy} = 3.45\times10^{-4}$$

Adding Equations (2.20) and (2.21) gives:

$$5\times10^{-4} = \varepsilon_x + \varepsilon_y - \frac{1}{2}\varepsilon_x + \frac{1}{2}\varepsilon_y$$

$$5\times10^{-4} = \frac{1}{2}\varepsilon_x + \frac{3}{2}\varepsilon_y$$

And finally, substituting for ε_x:

$$5\times10^{-4} - 3\times10^{-4} = \frac{3}{2}\varepsilon_y$$

$$\varepsilon_y = \frac{4}{3}\times10^{-3}$$

The required strains are $\varepsilon_x = 6 \times 10^{-4}$, $\varepsilon_y = 1.33 \times 10^{-4}$ and $\gamma_{xy} = 3.45 \times 10^{-4}$.

Once the full state of strain is known with reference to the xy-coordinate system, the principal strains or maximum shear strains can then be determined directly from the transformation equations or by using Mohr's circle.

EXERCISE 2.11

A 45° strain gauge rosette gives the readings shown in Figure 2.34. Determine the maximum and minimum values of direct strain, the maximum shear strain and the directions in which they act.

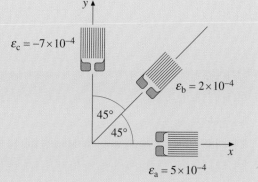

Figure 2.34   Direct strains from the elements of a 45° strain gauge rosette

SAQ 2.13 (Learning outcomes 2.1, 2.3 and 2.8)

A $60°$ strain gauge rosette gives the readings shown in Figure 2.35. Find the principal strains, the maximum shear strain and the directions in which they act.

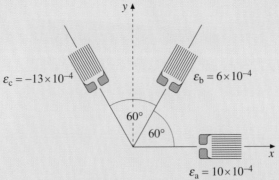

Figure 2.35   Direct strains from the elements of a $60°$ strain gauge rosette

This section has presented a lot of equations in quick succession, so I'll emphasize again that they're *not* to be memorized. They are vital if you ever need to interpret data from strain gauges, and importantly they can be used to gain additional information by the use of the constitutive equations you met earlier. The following questions will help you to appreciate this.

SAQ 2.14 (Learning outcomes 2.1, 2.4, 2.6 and 2.8)

Recall that strains can be converted to stresses using the appropriate constitutive equations, assuming linear-elastic deformation (see Section 5). If the strains you determined in your answer to Exercise 2.11 were measured in stainless steel ($E = 190$ GPa, $v = 0.3$), what were the principal stresses in this component?

SAQ 2.15 (Learning outcomes 2.1, 2.4, 2.6 and 2.8)

A $45°$ strain gauge rosette as shown in Figure 2.31 (i.e. two gauges at $90°$ with a third at $45°$ to the other two) is mounted on a laptop screen to measure the effect of the laptop being inadvertently sat upon (Figure 2.36). The strains measured during the test were:

$\varepsilon_a = 400 \times 10^{-6}$

$\varepsilon_b = 150 \times 10^{-6}$

$\varepsilon_c = 220 \times 10^{-6}$.

The screen is made from polycarbonate with properties $E = 2.2$ GPa and $v = 0.38$.

Calculate:

(a) the values of the principal strains in the screen

(b) the values of the principal stresses in the screen

(c) the strain ε_z normal to the screen.

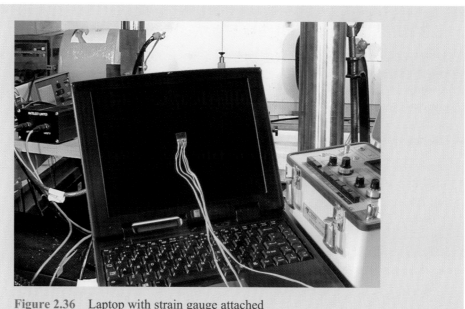

Figure 2.36   Laptop with strain gauge attached

The next section wraps up our introduction to stress and strain by looking at an example of a failure where such analyses were deployed, and where the cause was linked to a problem in material specification and design. Strains and stresses are important because exceeding certain limits imposed by a material's strength or the specifications of a design can and will lead to failure – and that is what a good design will avoid.

7 FREIGHT CONTAINER CASE STUDY

The majority of goods traded globally nowadays are packed in large boxes of standard sizes and moved to their destinations by road, rail or sea. There are something like 20 million of these *freight containers* (Figure 2.37) worldwide. The use of containers helps to minimize labour-intensive handling of goods, offers protection to the cargo and makes efficient use of available storage space, especially when they are stacked one upon the other.

All commercial containers are built according to the same principles, laid down by the International Organization for Standardization (ISO). Essentially, freight containers are panelled boxes, supported by a strong rectangular framework of horizontal and vertical members that are connected at each corner by standardized fittings. The corner fittings are important because they act as feet for the container to stand on and allow the containers to be stacked one upon the other; they also incorporate standard holes for lifting and for securing the container during transit.

Here, we're going to look at a particular maritime freight container, an early design similar to that in Figure 2.38, that wasn't quite up to doing its job. The fully loaded container was being lifted by a crane on the quayside when a docker noticed that a long tear had developed along the (riveted) joints in one of the side panels. The tear followed the dashed line superimposed on Figure 2.38. At the time, the container was loaded with metal castings to about 90% of its rated capacity. There was no general collapse of the structure: the cargo remained inside, but was vulnerable to the elements and to thieves, and so the container had to be withdrawn from service and its contents transferred. In the following weeks this pattern of events was repeated at locations scattered randomly across the trade routes of the world, and the associated costs to the shipping company began to escalate alarmingly. As it turned out, all the failed containers had been made at the same factory over a period of about a month.

Figure 2.37 Freight containers

Figure 2.38 Container showing the position of the tear in the side wall and along the top rail

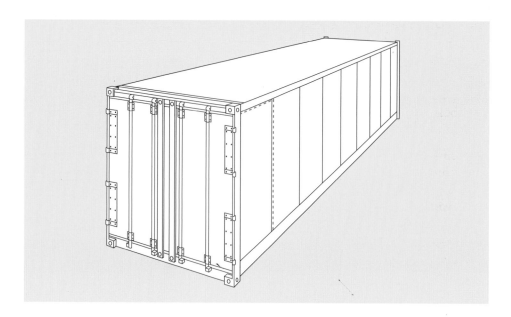

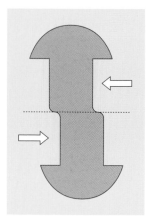

Figure 2.39 The shape of a fractured rivet

The container side walls consisted of sheets of aluminium alloy attached to one another and to the steel framework by riveting along vertical lap joints. To these sheets were riveted vertical 'top-hat' channels, i.e. strips of metal folded over so that their cross sections resemble that of a top hat, which act to stiffen the container walls. Subsequent examination of the rivets by a metallurgist, hired by the shipping company, indicated that, typically, one half had been displaced transversely relative to the other half, as sketched in Figure 2.39. This means that highly localized shear deformation in a single plane must have occurred.

To help understand how this must have come about, it is possible to imagine the container as a hollow beam, supported at its corner fittings and subjected to loading due to the weight of the internal cargo. This loading causes bending of the container so that it sags along its length, as sketched in Figure 2.40 (the deflection is exaggerated here). In fact, deflection of the container in this way is perfectly normal and acceptable, provided it remains within limits stipulated in the ISO guidelines for the structure. The limits are imposed to ensure that deformation remains entirely

Figure 2.40 Model of the container as a beam showing the forces acting near a joint

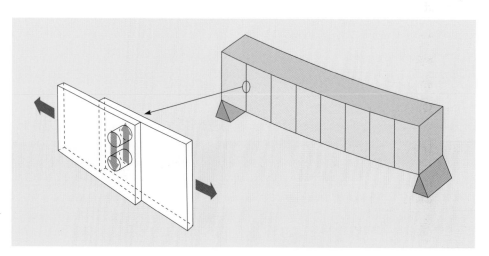

elastic, so that no permanent plastic damage occurs during normal use. The important thing here is that the bending generates shear forces, and hence shear stresses, that cause the overlapping side panels to slide past each other; these stresses have components in both the horizontal and vertical directions see Figure 2.40 and vary from place to place across the section. On the other hand, the sides of the containers, its panels and rivets, are specifically designed to bear these shear stresses. So the question remains: why did the rivets fail in this case?

As well as hiring a professional metallurgist, the shipping company also employed a structural engineer to carry out an assessment of the overall integrity and design of the container, including a stress analysis. However, the freight container is a composite structure consisting of aluminium panels attached to a complex steel framework. The contrasting Young's moduli of these materials make even the elastic deformation of the structure highly non-uniform. As well as shear deformation in the side panels, there is a tendency for the wall to buckle under an applied vertical load. These features make a theoretical analysis of the structure difficult. It is possible to construct a finite element model of the entire container along with its loading boundary conditions, but in this case the consultant engineer decided it would be quicker and more cost effective to infer the stresses from experimental measurements made on a fully loaded container that was hoisted up vertically.

The first step taken by the engineer was to reveal the distribution of strains in the vicinity of the riveted joints that were prone to fail. By initially using a 'full field' measurement technique it was possible to locate the problem area where the strains, and hence the stresses, were highest. A second, more precise, 'point' measurement technique was then employed in order to determine the state of strain within this smaller area. In this case, a photoelastic coating was used for the initial field assessment. With the site of the highest strain located, the magnitude of the strain was then measured by using resistance strain gauges.

> Note that such shear is always associated with bending. We don't need to consider bending for this analysis, but I will cover it more thoroughly in Block 1 Part 6.

SAQ 2.16 (Learning outcomes 2.1, 2.6, 2.8 and 2.9)

Strain measurements were made on one of the side panels, close to the riveted lap joint, as shown in Figure 2.41. The magnitudes of the direct strains were found to be:

strain along OA = 11×10^{-5}

strain along OB = 117×10^{-5}

strain along OC = -19×10^{-5}.

(a) Determine the direct and shear components of strain referred to axes OA and OC.

(b) If the panel is deformed elastically, what are the corresponding components of stress? (The panel is made from an aluminium alloy with a Young's modulus of 65.5 GPa, a shear modulus of 25 GPa and a Poisson's ratio of 0.33.)

(c) What is the maximum shear stress in the plane of the plate?

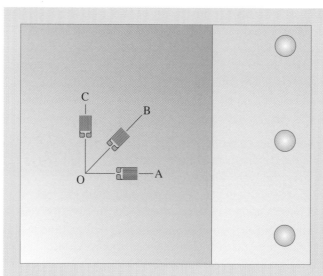

Figure 2.41   Location of strain measurements near a join on the container side panel

Next, the investigating engineer wanted to know what the actual load-carrying ability of the rivets was just prior to failure, and whether this was adequate for the job. For this the *shear strength* of the rivets is required, i.e. the shear stress necessary to cause the rivets to fail.

Shear strength measurement is not straightforward, but it is possible to infer the mechanical strength of the rivet by using one of the standard methods for ☑ **hardness testing** ☑, which can be carried out on a small, undamaged area of the broken rivet. Hardness readings can then be converted to shear strength by means of an empirical correlation between hardness and shear strength for the particular alloy in question. For many commercial alloys in common use, such information is often available in graphical form, or exists as a look-up table, in the manufacturers' data sheets.

> Shear testing is difficult because of the need to restrain the sample in such a way that no bending or normal stress contributes to the failure.

☑ Hardness testing

Hardness, in its engineering sense, generally signifies the resistance of a material to cutting, indentation or abrasion. It is usually quantified by measuring the impression made in the surface of a material by an indenter of known geometry with a known applied force: the smaller the resulting indent, the harder the material is. Hardness is related to the strength of a material: a material will respond elastically to the indenter until the applied force reaches the yield strength, after which plastic flow begins and an indent is made. There are empirical relationships between hardness scales and strength,

although converting between hardness and strength in this way is not necessarily accurate or reliable.

Several standard methods of testing for hardness exist, each with its own measurement scales. These include Brinell, which uses a spherical steel indenter, and Vickers (Figure 2.42), which uses a pyramid-shaped diamond indenter.

To use the standard Vickers test a diamond pyramid is pressed down onto a flat and polished surface of the specimen (Figure 2.42). A standard load F is used to impress the indenter and the size of   ▷

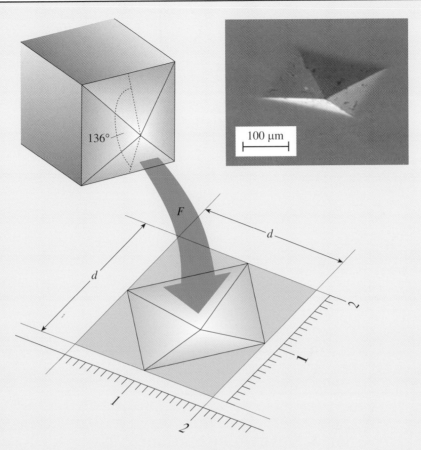

Figure 2.42 Schematic illustration of the Vickers hardness test; scanning electron micrograph of a pyramid-shaped indent in steel (insert)

the indentation produced is measured. The Vickers tests expresses the hardness as a number H_V which is simply the load divided by the surface area of the indentation. In terms of the load F (kg) and the average length d (mm) of the diagonals of the indentation, the hardness number is:

$$H_V = \frac{2F \sin(\phi/2)}{d^2}$$

where the quantity ϕ is the angle between the opposite faces of the indenter. A standard value of 136° is used, for which

$$H_V = \frac{1.854F}{d^2}$$

Hardness values are often measured simply by using reference tables rather than following through the calculation. Modern indenter systems can make hundreds of indents on a surface automatically to allow average values or even maps of hardness to be obtained, although determination of the indent size still needs a human (the more indents that are made, the more bored the human becomes …). Figure 2.43 shows a hardness map obtained along two lines through the thickness of a welded aluminium plate. Large changes in hardness can be seen from the fusion zone (FZ; where the metal was melted) through the heat-affected zone (HAZ) to the parent plate.

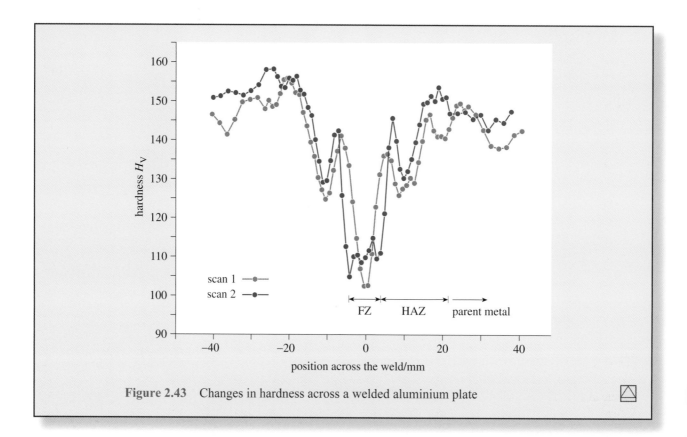

Figure 2.43   Changes in hardness across a welded aluminium plate

SAQ 2.17 (Learning outcome 2.9)

Figure 2.44 shows an empirical correlation between hardness number, tensile strength and shear strength for the aluminium–copper alloy used in the failed freight-container rivets. Note that broad bands have been used to represent uncertainty in the correlation. Table 2.7 shows the results from a number of Vickers hardness measurements carried out on samples of sheared rivets from the container itself.

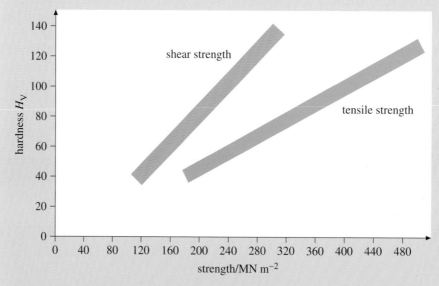

Figure 2.44   Correlation of hardness with the tensile and shear strengths for alloy HR15 (Al, 4.4% Cu, 0.8% Si, 0.8% Mn, 0.4% Mg)

Table 2.7 Tests on rivets from a failed container

Sample number	Hardness H_V
1	63.9
2	58.4
3	57.5
4	56.2
5	61.8
6	64.4
7	63.3
8	59.3
9	64.9
10	66.0
Mean	61.6

The specified tensile strength of new (undamaged) rivets was 385 MPa. Use the correlation graph (Figure 2.44) and test data (Table 2.7) to determine whether the mean strength of the failed rivets meets this specification by completing Table 2.8.

Table 2.8 Comparison of new and failed rivets

	Hardness H_V	Tensile strength/ MPa	Shear strength/MPa
New rivets		385	
Failed rivets			

Now, if you compare the shear strength of the faulty rivets with the maximum shear stress you derived from the strain gauge measurements in SAQ 2.16, you will see that the rivet strength is actually much greater than the measured stress. But hold on: the strain gauges were attached to the panelling, so the stress you calculated was that in the panel, not in the rivet. To figure out the stress in the rivets it is necessary to know a little more information about the rivet size and spacing.

The stress in one panel was transmitted to the next panel by rivets of 4.75 mm diameter spaced 50 mm apart (i.e. with 50 mm between their centres), as sketched in Figure 2.45. Recall that the shear stress you calculated with respect to the axes of the strain gauges, $\tau_{xy} = 60.5$ MPa, coincided closely with the maximum shear stress in the plate. Hence, we can use this as the limiting stress acting on the cross section of the plate.

Figure 2.45
Arrangement of riveted
panel joint

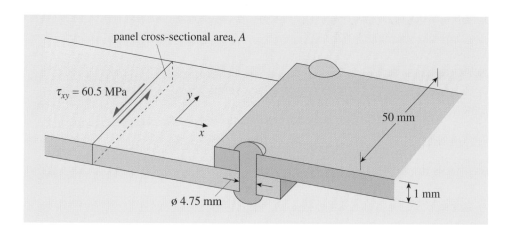

SAQ 2.18 (Learning outcome 2.9)

(a) Referring to Figure 2.45, calculate the shear force in the y-direction acting in the cross section of the panel.

(b) Assuming that this force is transmitted from a 50 mm length of one panel to the next by *one rivet* (note that each rivet shares a 50 mm section with an adjoining rivet), calculate the shear stress in a rivet.

Hence, the shear strength of the faulty rivets (160 MPa) is lower than the shear stress experienced by new rivets during the experimental tests carried out by the engineer on a fully loaded container (171 MPa). A stress greater than the material's strength will inevitably lead to failure.

It was discovered that a crucial heat treatment had been omitted during fabrication of the rivets, resulting in the low strength. This is clearly something that applies only to the batch of containers that used the faulty rivets and it might have been expected that normal production of the containers could then resume. However, in compiling a final report, the investigating engineer expressed concern that even the shear strength of undamaged rivets (225 MPa) left little margin for error. Usually, engineering structures are built such that there is a considerable margin of safety incorporated at the design stage. This is to allow for such effects as transient loading that is higher than experienced when the container is static, as might occur when the container is being lifted or moved, or when it is set down heavily in transit, for example. A large enough safety factor would have allowed even for low-strength rivets.

It is significant that this freight container was being lifted by crane when the shearing failure was observed by a docker. If a crane bumps a container while lifting, this will induce a transient vertical load well in excess of the gross weight of the container. Again, ISO guidelines require large-scale tests on new containers to ensure they can cope with any *foreseeable* loading condition, but the integrity of the overall structure always relies on that of its smaller components.

To allow for the unknown, it is usual in design to speak in terms of a ☒ **factor of safety** ☒ (or safety factor), which is usually the ratio of static strength of a component to the static load that it is expected to sustain. In this case the factor of safety for new rivets was $225/171 = 1.3$, which the investigators thought was far too low. However, they also judged that the overall design of the containers was adequate and so the manufacturers were able to implement a small change in the safety factor associated with the panel joints in order to ensure the future structural integrity of their containers. You can round off this section by working out that design change for yourself in the following question.

SAQ 2.19 (Learning outcome 2.9)

Using the same rivet alloy, what diameter of rivet would you use in the freight-container panel joints in order to keep the static factor of safety for shear loading to just above 2.0?

☒ Factor of safety

The static factor of safety of a component is defined as:

$$\frac{\text{static strength of the component}}{\text{static load on the component}}$$

Here 'strength' means the maximum value of load that the component can bear in a given situation (e.g. in tension, compression or shear; whichever is deemed most appropriate) without failing. 'Static' implies that the loads are assumed to be constant and do not vary with time. The factor of safety must be large enough to cover the uncertainties in strength and loading, which is why it is sometimes referred to rudely as a 'factor of ignorance'.

The magnitude of the factor of safety depends on a number of things. These include the certainty with which the design process can predict likely stresses, how well the mechanical properties of the individual components are known, and also the need to ensure absolute safety. A factor of safety of 1.0 implies that there is absolutely no margin of safety at all. In fact, the lowest real factors of safety occur in aerospace engineering, where rigorous testing and quality control, coupled with the necessity to keep the weight and size of components to a minimum, means that safety factors are often in the range 1.25–1.5. In more general cases where material properties are well known, and stresses are quantifiable with some certainty, values in the range of 1.5–2.5 are usual. If impact or shock loading is possible, then safety factors of ≥3 can be expected. If a design can be made with an even greater margin without compromising cost or weight, then even higher safety factors may be used. ◺

8 SUMMARY

The first two parts of this course have introduced you to dealing with the concepts of stress and strain, which are fundamental to the analysis of the integrity of any product, component or structure. You will revisit and reuse these concepts continually as we progress through descriptions of how structures behave and what happens if they fail.

In Block 1 Part 3 we will look at failure modes: the consequences of exceeding strength limits. It is accurate stress analysis that allows this to be avoided.

LEARNING OUTCOMES

After you have studied Block 1 Part 2 you should be able to do the following.

2.1 Describe and quantify normal and shear strains as a means of measuring deformation in engineering components and structures.

2.2 Understand thermal and other stress-free strains and perform outline calculations with them.

2.3 Understand and apply two-dimensional and three-dimensional descriptions of strain, including the use of tensor notation.

2.4 Understand and apply the two-dimensional plane strain and plane stress approximations in simplifying three-dimensional engineering structures.

2.5 Use plane strain transformation equations, or Mohr's circle, to analyse the two-dimensional state of strain at a point in a material body.

2.6 Appreciate constitutive equations as a means of relating stress to strain via material properties, and use them to analyse the elastic response of materials under plane stress and plane strain.

2.7 Interpret and analyse isochromatic fringe patterns in photoelastic models of simple engineering structures under stress.

2.8 Carry out analyses of 45° and 60° rosette strain gauge data.

2.9 Use stress, strain and strength concepts in the analysis of materials failures.

ANSWERS TO EXERCISES

EXERCISE 2.1

(a) The strain in the bar is:

$$\varepsilon = \frac{\Delta L}{L} = \frac{0.1\,\text{mm}}{100\,\text{mm}} = 0.001$$

This is equivalent to 0.1% or 1000$\mu\varepsilon$.

(b) The change in length of the bar is given by:

$$\Delta L = \varepsilon L = 0.001 \times 300\,\text{mm} = 0.3\,\text{mm}$$

Total length = 300.3 mm.

EXERCISE 2.2

(a) In tension:

$$\varepsilon = \frac{\Delta L}{L} = \frac{13\,\text{cm} - 10\,\text{cm}}{10\,\text{cm}} = 0.30$$

(b) In compression:

$$\varepsilon = \frac{\Delta L}{L} = \frac{10\,\text{cm} - 13\,\text{cm}}{13\,\text{cm}} = -0.23$$

EXERCISE 2.3

Recall the sign convention that I established in Block 1 Part 1, Section 5.2. A shear stress is positive if it acts in a positive direction on the positive face of an element. Both the shear stresses τ_{xy} and τ_{yx} do this, so they are positive shear stresses. The shear strain arising from them must, therefore, be positive also.

EXERCISE 2.4

Using Table 2.3, the compressive strength of concrete is −60 MPa. Half of this is −30 MPa, and using $E = 19$ GPa:

$$\text{Strain: } \varepsilon = \frac{\sigma}{E} = \frac{-30 \times 10^6\,\text{Pa}}{19 \times 10^9\,\text{Pa}} = -0.0016$$

Change in length: $\Delta L = \varepsilon L = -0.0016 \times 10\,\text{m} = -0.016\,\text{m} = -16\,\text{mm}$

EXERCISE 2.5

Axial strain:

$$\varepsilon_x = \frac{\sigma_x}{E} = \frac{100 \times 10^6 \text{ Pa}}{210 \times 10^9 \text{ Pa}} = 4.76 \times 10^{-4}$$

Lateral strain:

$$\varepsilon_y = \varepsilon_z = -v\varepsilon_x = -0.3 \times 4.76 \times 10^{-4} = -1.43 \times 10^{-4}$$

EXERCISE 2.6

The maximum stress difference occurs where the fringe order is greatest, i.e. where $N = 27$:

$$\sigma_1 - \sigma_2 = \frac{Nf}{t} = \frac{27 \times 9.5 \times 10^3 \text{ N m}^{-1}}{5 \times 10^{-3} \text{ m}} = 51 \text{ MPa}$$

EXERCISE 2.7

As L gets larger, the cross sectional area A gets smaller. Considering $R = \rho L/A$, both these dimensional changes contribute to an increase in resistance.

EXERCISE 2.8

The resistance in the wire is:

$$R = \frac{\rho L}{A} = \frac{0.017 \times 10^{-6} \text{ } \Omega \text{ m} \times 5 \times 10^{-3} \text{ m}}{\pi \left(0.25 \times 10^{-3}\right)^2 \text{ m}^2} = 4.33 \times 10^{-4} \text{ } \Omega$$

wrong

Rearranging Equation (2.16):

$$\Delta R = K\varepsilon R = 2 \times 5 \times 10^{-6} \times 4.33 \times 10^{-4} \text{ } \Omega = 4.33 \times 10^{-9} \text{ } \Omega$$

EXERCISE 2.9

$\Delta R = K\varepsilon R$, so large values of both sensitivity factor K and initial resistance R would be an advantage since they would increase ΔR for any given strain. (In fact K does not vary much for most metals, so this is not really a useful option.) To make R large the wire needs to be long, thin and made from a material with high resistivity ($R = \rho L/A$).

EXERCISE 2.10

The principal strains are given by:

$$\varepsilon_{1,2} = \frac{\varepsilon_x + \varepsilon_y}{2} \pm \sqrt{\left(\frac{\varepsilon_x - \varepsilon_y}{2}\right)^2 + \left(\frac{\gamma_{xy}}{2}\right)^2}$$

$$= \left[\left(\frac{9+1}{2}\right) \pm \sqrt{\left(\frac{9-1}{2}\right)^2 + \left(\frac{-8}{2}\right)^2}\right] \times 10^{-4}$$

$$= (5 \pm 5.66) \times 10^{-4}$$

$$\varepsilon_1 = 10.66 \times 10^{-4}$$
$$\varepsilon_2 = -0.66 \times 10^{-4}$$

The orientations of the principal axes are given by:

$$\tan 2\theta_p = \frac{\gamma_{xy}}{\varepsilon_x - \varepsilon_y} = \frac{-8}{8} = -1$$

$$2\theta_p = -45°, 135°$$
$$\theta_p = -22.5°, 67.5°$$

Using our sign convention, a negative angle indicates a clockwise rotation from the x-direction.

The maximum shear strain is:

$$\frac{\gamma_{max}}{2} = \pm\sqrt{\left(\frac{\varepsilon_x - \varepsilon_y}{2}\right)^2 + \left(\frac{\gamma_{xy}}{2}\right)^2} = \left[\pm\sqrt{\left(\frac{8}{2}\right)^2 + \left(\frac{-8}{2}\right)^2}\right] \times 10^{-4}$$

$$\gamma_{max} = \pm 11.31 \times 10^{-4}$$

EXERCISE 2.11

By inspection, $\varepsilon_x = 5 \times 10^{-4}$ and $\varepsilon_y = -7 \times 10^{-4}$.

Substituting 2×10^{-4} at $\theta = 45°$ into the transformation equation gives:

$$2 \times 10^{-4} = \frac{1}{2}(5-7)10^{-4} + 0 + \left(\frac{\gamma_{xy}}{2} \times 1\right)$$

$$\gamma_{xy} = 6 \times 10^{-4}$$

To find the principal planes:

$$\tan 2\theta_p = \frac{\gamma_{xy}}{\varepsilon_x - \varepsilon_y}$$

$$\theta_p = 13.3°, \ 103.3°$$

Substituting these values into the transformation equation gives:

$$\varepsilon_{13.3°} = \frac{1}{2}\left(-2\times10^{-4}\right) + \frac{1}{2}\left(12\times10^{-4}\right)(+0.89) + \frac{6\times10^{-4}}{2}(+0.45)$$

$$= 5.69\times10^{-4}$$

$$\varepsilon_{103.3°} = \frac{1}{2}\left(-2\times10^{-4}\right) + \frac{1}{2}\left(12\times10^{-4}\right)(-0.89) + \frac{6\times10^{-4}}{2}(-0.45)$$

$$= -7.69\times10^{-4}$$

Thus:

$$\varepsilon_1 = 5.69\times10^{-4} \text{ at } 13.3°$$

$$\varepsilon_2 = -7.69\times10^{-4} \text{ at } 103.3°$$

The maximum shear strain is:

$$\frac{\gamma_{max}}{2} = \pm\sqrt{\left(\frac{\varepsilon_x - \varepsilon_y}{2}\right)^2 + \left(\frac{\gamma_{xy}}{2}\right)^2}$$

$$\gamma_{max} = \pm2\sqrt{\left(\frac{12\times10^{-4}}{2}\right)^2 + \left(\frac{6\times10^{-4}}{2}\right)^2} = \pm13.42\times10^{-4}$$

The planes of maximum shear strain occur at 45° to the principal stress directions:

$$\theta_s = -31.7°, 58.3°.$$

The graphical solution is given in Figure 2.46.

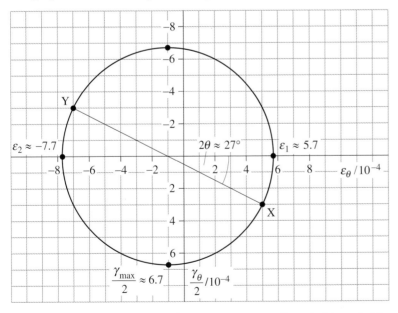

Figure 2.46   Mohr's strain circle for the gauge readings in Figure 2.34

ANSWERS TO SELF-ASSESSMENT QUESTIONS

SAQ 2.1

(a) $\Delta L = \varepsilon L = -0.0007 \times 2.0 \text{ m} = -0.0014 \text{ m}$

Final length $= L + \Delta L = 1.9986 \text{ m}$

(b) $\sigma = \dfrac{F}{A} = \dfrac{-130 \times 10^3 \text{ N}}{50 \times 10^{-3} \times 50 \times 10^{-3} \text{ m}^2} = -52 \text{ MPa}$

SAQ 2.2

(a) Longitudinal engineering strain:

$$\varepsilon_x = \frac{\Delta L}{L} = \frac{65 \text{ mm}}{100 \text{ mm}} = 0.65$$

Transverse engineering strain:

$$\varepsilon_y = \frac{\Delta w}{w} = \frac{-3 \text{ mm}}{14 \text{ mm}} = -0.21$$

(b) Longitudinal true strain:

$$\varepsilon_x = \ln\left(\frac{L_1}{L_0}\right) = \ln\left(\frac{165}{100}\right) = 0.50$$

Transverse true strain:

$$\varepsilon_y = \ln\left(\frac{w_1}{w_0}\right) = \ln\left(\frac{11}{14}\right) = -0.24$$

SAQ 2.3

$\Delta L = 120 \times 10^{-3} \text{ m} \times 15 \times 10^{-6} \text{ }°\text{C}^{-1} \times 850 \text{ }°\text{C} = 1.53 \times 10^{-3} \text{ m or } 1.53 \text{ mm.}$

SAQ 2.4

The thin disc has two free surfaces across which no stress can be transmitted; hence, to a good approximation $\sigma_z = 0$ throughout the disc. Therefore, a state of plane stress exists in the plane perpendicular to the z-direction.

SAQ 2.5

Since there is no displacement in the z-direction a state of plane strain exists in a plane normal to this direction.

SAQ 2.6

(a) As a check, the stress resulting from this load is:

$$\sigma = \frac{F}{A} = \frac{(3000 \times 9.8)\,\text{N}}{300 \times 10^{-6}\,\text{m}^2} = 98\,\text{MPa}$$

This is below the yield stress, so we can use $\sigma = E\varepsilon$ and $E = 206$ GPa to determine the strain:

$$\varepsilon = \frac{\sigma}{E} = \frac{98 \times 10^6\,\text{Pa}}{206 \times 10^9\,\text{Pa}} = 4.76 \times 10^{-4}$$

Thus, the extension is:

$$\Delta L = \varepsilon L = 4.76 \times 10^{-4} \times 2000\,\text{m} = 0.95\,\text{m}$$

(b) $\Delta L = L\alpha\Delta T = 2000\,\text{m} \times 10 \times 10^{-6}\,°\text{C}^{-1} \times -15\,°\text{C} = -0.3\,\text{m}$

so the cable contracts by 300 mm.

SAQ 2.7

Given $\sigma_x = -2$ MPa, $\sigma_y = -10$ MPa, $\tau_{xy} = 0.5$ MPa and $\varepsilon_z = 0$ (plane strain), first rearrange Equation (2.8) to obtain σ_z:

$$\sigma_z = E\varepsilon_z + v(\sigma_x + \sigma_y)$$
$$= 0 + 0.2(-2 - 10)\,\text{MPa}$$
$$= -2.4\,\text{MPa}$$

Then, obtain ε_x and ε_y from Equations (2.6) and (2.7):

$$\varepsilon_x = \frac{\sigma_x}{E} - \frac{v}{E}(\sigma_y + \sigma_z)$$
$$= \frac{-2 \times 10^6}{19 \times 10^9} - \frac{0.2}{19 \times 10^9}(-10 - 2.4) \times 10^6$$
$$= 25\,\mu\varepsilon$$

$$\varepsilon_y = \frac{\sigma_y}{E} - \frac{v}{E}(\sigma_x + \sigma_z)$$
$$= \frac{-10 \times 10^6}{19 \times 10^9} - \frac{0.2}{19 \times 10^9}(-2 - 2.4) \times 10^6$$
$$= -480\,\mu\varepsilon$$

and finally from Equations (2.9) and (2.10):

$$G = \frac{E}{2(1+v)} = \frac{19}{2(1+0.2)}\,\text{GPa} = 7.9\,\text{GPa}$$

$$\gamma_{xy} = \frac{\tau_{xy}}{G} = \frac{0.5 \times 10^6}{7.9 \times 10^9} = 63\,\mu\varepsilon$$

The full strain tensor is therefore:

$$\begin{bmatrix} 25 & 63 & 0 \\ 63 & -480 & 0 \\ 0 & 0 & 0 \end{bmatrix} \mu\varepsilon$$

SAQ 2.8

$\sigma_1 = 111$ MPa, $\sigma_2 = -11$ MPa, and for plane stress $\sigma_3 = 0$, so there are three non-zero principal strains:

$$\varepsilon_1 = \frac{1}{E}(\sigma_1 - v\sigma_2) = \frac{1}{210 \times 10^9}\left[111 - 0.3(-11)\right] \times 10^6 = \frac{114.3}{210 \times 10^3} = 5.44 \times 10^{-4}$$

$$\varepsilon_2 = \frac{1}{E}(\sigma_2 - v\sigma_1) = \frac{1}{210 \times 10^9}\left[-11 - 0.3(111)\right] \times 10^6 = \frac{-44.3}{210 \times 10^3} = -2.11 \times 10^{-4}$$

$$\varepsilon_3 = \frac{-v}{E}(\sigma_1 + \sigma_2) = \frac{-0.3}{210 \times 10^9}\left[111 + (-11)\right] \times 10^6 = \frac{-30.0}{210 \times 10^3} = -1.43 \times 10^{-4}$$

SAQ 2.9

The strain directions measured are assumed to be the principal axes and so there are no shear strains: $\varepsilon_1 = \varepsilon_x$, $\varepsilon_2 = \varepsilon_y$ and $\varepsilon_3 = \varepsilon_z$. So the tensor is:

$$\begin{bmatrix} 3200 & 0 & 0 \\ 0 & -450 & 0 \\ 0 & 0 & -920 \end{bmatrix} \times 10^{-6}$$

The principal stresses are calculated using Equations (2.14)–(2.16), thus:

$$\sigma_1 = \frac{E}{(1+v)(1-2v)}\left[(1-v)\varepsilon_1 + v\varepsilon_2 + v\varepsilon_3\right]$$

$$= \frac{70 \times 10^9}{(1+0.3)(1-0.6)}\left[(1-0.3)(3200 \times 10^{-6}) + (0.3 \times -450 \times 10^{-6}) + (0.3 \times -920 \times 10^{-6})\right]$$

$$= 246 \text{ MPa}$$

And likewise, $\sigma_2 = 50$ MPa and $\sigma_3 = 24$ MPa.

The stress tensor is then written as:

$$\begin{bmatrix} 246 & 0 & 0 \\ 0 & 50 & 0 \\ 0 & 0 & 24 \end{bmatrix} \text{MPa}$$

SAQ 2.10

(a) The neck has cross-sectional dimensions of 15 mm by 6 mm and is loaded by a force of 120 N; the average stress is:

$$\sigma = \frac{F}{A} = \frac{120 \text{ N}}{15 \times 10^{-3} \times 6 \times 10^{-3} \text{ m}^2} = 1.3 \text{ MPa}$$

If this stress is uniaxial then $\sigma_1 = \sigma$ and $\sigma_2 = \sigma_3 = 0$, hence $(\sigma_1 - \sigma_2) = 1.3$ MPa.

(b) (i) There are five dark fringes visible to the right of the zero-order fringe (the last one is right on the edge), thus:

$$\sigma_1 - \sigma_2 = \frac{Nf}{t} = \frac{5 \times 9.5 \times 10^3}{6 \times 10^{-3}} = 7.9 \text{ MPa}$$

(ii) I count eight dark fringes to the left of the zero-order fringe (it is arguable whether there is a hint of a ninth fringe just starting).

For eight fringes: $\sigma_1 - \sigma_2 = 12.7$ MPa.

(For nine fringes: $\sigma_1 - \sigma_2 = 14.3$ MPa.)

(c) At the outer edge the stress has been magnified by a factor of $7.9/1.3 = 6.1$.

At the inner edge the ratio is $12.7/1.3 = 9.8$ (or 11.0 for nine fringes).

SAQ 2.11

For the finite element model:

outer-edge magnification ratio is $300/50 = 6$

inner-edge magnification ratio is $500/50 = 10$.

These ratios are very similar to those computed in part (c) for the epoxy hook.

Information about the stress distribution deduced from a photoelastic model can be satisfactorily compared with that in a component of different scale, even when the materials from which they are assumed to be made are different.

SAQ 2.12

The calculated principal strains and orientations are:

$$\varepsilon_{1,2} = \frac{\varepsilon_x + \varepsilon_y}{2} \pm \sqrt{\left(\frac{\varepsilon_x - \varepsilon_y}{2}\right)^2 + \left(\frac{\gamma_{xy}}{2}\right)^2}$$

$$= \left[\left(\frac{7-5}{2}\right) \pm \sqrt{\left(\frac{7+5}{2}\right)^2 + \left(\frac{8}{2}\right)^2}\right] \times 10^{-4}$$

$$= (1 \pm 7.21) \times 10^{-4}$$

$$\varepsilon_1 = 8.21 \times 10^{-4}$$

$$\varepsilon_2 = -6.21 \times 10^{-4}$$

$$\tan 2\theta_p = \frac{\gamma_{xy}}{\varepsilon_x - \varepsilon_y} = \frac{8}{7-(-5)} = 0.667$$

$$\theta_p = 16.9°, 106.9°$$

Your graphical solution should look something like Figure 2.47:

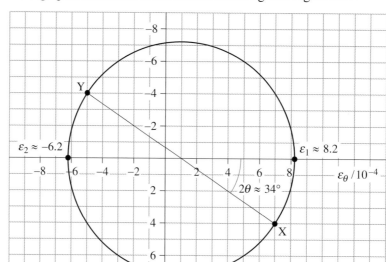

Figure 2.47   Mohr's circle for the strains $\varepsilon_x = 7 \times 10^{-4}$, $\varepsilon_y = -5 \times 10^{-4}$ and $\gamma_{xy} = 8 \times 10^{-4}$

SAQ 2.13

We have $\varepsilon_x = \varepsilon_a = 10 \times 10^{-4}$. Substituting $\theta = 60°$, $\varepsilon_\theta = \varepsilon_b = 6 \times 10^{-4}$ into the transformation equation gives:

$$6 \times 10^{-4} = \frac{1}{2}\left(\varepsilon_x + \varepsilon_y\right) + \frac{1}{2}\left(\varepsilon_x - \varepsilon_y\right)(-0.5) + \frac{\gamma_{xy}}{2}(0.87)$$

and for $\theta = 120°$, $\varepsilon_\theta = \varepsilon_c = -13 \times 10^{-4}$:

$$-13 \times 10^{-4} = \frac{1}{2}\left(\varepsilon_x + \varepsilon_y\right) + \frac{1}{2}\left(\varepsilon_x - \varepsilon_y\right)(-0.5) + \frac{\gamma_{xy}}{2}(-0.87)$$

Subtracting the two equations gives:

$$19 \times 10^{-4} = 0.87\gamma_{xy}$$

$$\gamma_{xy} = 21.84 \times 10^{-4}$$

Adding the equations and then substituting for ε_y gives:

$$-7 \times 10^{-4} = \varepsilon_x + \varepsilon_y - \frac{1}{2}\varepsilon_x + \frac{1}{2}\varepsilon_y$$

$$-7 \times 10^{-4} = 5 \times 10^{-4} + \frac{3}{2}\varepsilon_y$$

$$\varepsilon_y = -8 \times 10^{-4}$$

To calculate the principal strains:

$$\varepsilon_{1,2} = \frac{\varepsilon_x + \varepsilon_y}{2} \pm \sqrt{\left(\frac{\varepsilon_x - \varepsilon_y}{2}\right)^2 + \left(\frac{\gamma_{xy}}{2}\right)^2}$$

$$= \frac{2 \times 10^{-4}}{2} \pm \sqrt{\left(\frac{18 \times 10^{-4}}{2}\right)^2 + \left(\frac{21.84 \times 10^{-4}}{2}\right)^2}$$

$$= 10^{-4} \pm 14.2 \times 10^{-4}$$

So $\varepsilon_1 = 15.2 \times 10^{-4}$ and $\varepsilon_2 = -13.2 \times 10^{-4}$.

The principal strain directions are found from:

$$\tan 2\theta_p = \frac{\gamma_{xy}}{\varepsilon_x - \varepsilon_y} = \frac{21.84}{18} = 1.213$$

So $\theta_p = 25.2°$, $115.2°$ and using substitution or Mohr's circle:

ε_1 is oriented at angle $\theta_p = 25.2°$.

ε_2 is oriented at angle $\theta_p = 115.2°$.

The maximum shear strain is given by:

$$\frac{\gamma_{max}}{2} = \pm \sqrt{\left(\frac{\varepsilon_x - \varepsilon_y}{2}\right)^2 + \left(\frac{\gamma_{xy}}{2}\right)^2}$$

$$= \pm \sqrt{\left(\frac{18 \times 10^{-4}}{2}\right)^2 + \left(\frac{21.84 \times 10^{-4}}{2}\right)^2}$$

$$= \pm 14.2 \times 10^{-4}$$

and the angles of the maximum shear strain are:

$$\tan 2\theta_s = -\frac{\varepsilon_x - \varepsilon_y}{\gamma_{xy}}$$

$$= \frac{18}{-21.84} = -0.824$$

$$\theta_s = -19.7°, \ 70.3°$$

SAQ 2.14

From Exercise 2.11 we have $\varepsilon_1 = 5.69 \times 10^{-4}$ and $\varepsilon_2 = -7.68 \times 10^{-4}$.

Since strain gauges are attached to a free surface, there is a state of plane stress and $\sigma_3 = 0$.

Using the plane stress equations of Table 2.4 we get:

$$\sigma_1 = \frac{190 \times 10^9}{1 - 0.3^2}(5.69 + 0.3 \times -7.68) \times 10^{-4} = 70.7 \text{ MPa}$$

$$\sigma_2 = \frac{190 \times 10^9}{1 - 0.3^2}(-7.68 + 0.3 \times 5.69) \times 10^{-4} = -125 \text{ MPa}$$

SAQ 2.15

(a) We have used a 45° gauge and so:
$$\varepsilon_x = \varepsilon_a = 400 \times 10^{-6}$$
$$\varepsilon_y = \varepsilon_c = 220 \times 10^{-6}$$
$$\varepsilon_{45°} = \varepsilon_b = 150 \times 10^{-6}.$$

Using the transformation equation:

$$\varepsilon_\theta = \frac{1}{2}\left(\varepsilon_x + \varepsilon_y\right) + \frac{1}{2}\left(\varepsilon_x - \varepsilon_y\right)\cos 2\theta + \frac{\gamma_{xy}}{2}\sin 2\theta$$

$$150 \times 10^{-6} = 310 \times 10^{-6} + 0 + \frac{\gamma_{xy}}{2}$$

So $\gamma_{xy} = -320 \times 10^{-6}$.

The principal strains are then found from:

$$\varepsilon_{1,2} = \frac{\varepsilon_x + \varepsilon_y}{2} \pm \sqrt{\left(\frac{\varepsilon_x - \varepsilon_y}{2}\right)^2 + \left(\frac{\gamma_{xy}}{2}\right)^2}$$

$$= \frac{620 \times 10^{-6}}{2} \pm \sqrt{\left(\frac{180 \times 10^{-6}}{2}\right)^2 + \left(\frac{-320 \times 10^{-6}}{2}\right)^2}$$

$$= 310 \times 10^{-6} \pm 184 \times 10^{-6}$$

So, $\varepsilon_1 = 494 \times 10^{-6}$ and $\varepsilon_2 = 126 \times 10^{-6}$.

(b) Acknowledging the fact that the strains are measured at a surface, which must by definition be in a state of plane stress, the principal stresses can be found using:

$$\sigma_1 = \frac{E}{1-v^2}\left(\varepsilon_1 + v\varepsilon_2\right) \text{ and } \sigma_2 = \frac{E}{1-v^2}\left(\varepsilon_2 + v\varepsilon_1\right)$$

Thus:

$$\sigma_1 = \frac{E}{1-v^2}\left(\varepsilon_1 + v\varepsilon_2\right)$$

$$= \frac{2.2 \times 10^9}{0.86}\left(494 \times 10^{-6} + 48 \times 10^{-6}\right)$$

$$= 1.4 \text{ MPa}$$

And similarly $\sigma_2 = 0.8$ MPa.

(c) The strain ε_z is equivalent to the third principal strain ε_3, and can be calculated from:

$$\varepsilon_3 = \frac{-v}{E}\left(\sigma_1 + \sigma_2\right)$$

$$= \frac{-0.38 \times 2.2 \times 10^6}{2.2 \times 10^9}$$

$$= -3.8 \times 10^{-4}$$

SAQ 2.16

(a) Choosing coordinate x- and y-axes to lie parallel to directions OA and OC respectively, by inspection:

along OA, $\varepsilon_x = 11 \times 10^{-5}$

along OC, $\varepsilon_y = -19 \times 10^{-5}$.

For the gauge aligned along OB, $\theta = 45°$ and $\varepsilon_\theta = 117 \times 10^{-5}$; hence:

$$\varepsilon_\theta = \frac{1}{2}\left(\varepsilon_x + \varepsilon_y\right) + \frac{\gamma_{xy}}{2}$$

$$\gamma_{xy} = 2\varepsilon_\theta - \varepsilon_x - \varepsilon_y = 242 \times 10^{-5}$$

The strain in the panel is therefore described by $\varepsilon_x = 11 \times 10^{-5}$, $\varepsilon_y = -19 \times 10^{-5}$ and $\gamma_{xy} = 242 \times 10^{-5}$.

(b) The elastic stresses and strains are related by Equations (2.10) and (2.11). Since the panel surface is 'free' $\sigma_z = 0$, so:

$$\varepsilon_x = \frac{1}{E}\left(\sigma_x - v\sigma_y\right)$$

$$\varepsilon_y = \frac{1}{E}\left(\sigma_y - v\sigma_x\right)$$

$$\gamma_{xy} = \frac{1}{G}\tau_{xy}$$

We know the strains and the elastic constants E, G, and v, so we have three equations which can be solved for the three unknown components of stress.

The last equation gives:

$$\tau_{xy} = G\gamma_{xy}$$
$$= 25 \times 10^9 \text{ Pa} \times 242 \times 10^{-5}$$
$$= 60.5 \text{ MPa}$$

Solving the other two equations:

$$\sigma_x = \frac{E}{1 - v^2}\left(\varepsilon_x + v\varepsilon_y\right)$$
$$= \frac{65.5 \times 10^9}{1 - 0.33^2}\left(11 - 0.33 \times 19\right) \times 10^{-5}$$
$$= 3.5 \text{ MPa}$$

$$\sigma_y = \frac{E}{1 - v^2}\left(\varepsilon_y + v\varepsilon_x\right) = -11.3 \text{ MPa (a compressive stress)}$$

The stress in the panel is described by $\sigma_x = 3.5$ MPa, $\sigma_y = -11.3$ MPa and $\gamma_{xy} = 60.5$ MPa.

(c) The maximum shear stress is:

$$\tau_{max} = \pm\sqrt{\left(\frac{\sigma_x - \sigma_y}{2}\right)^2 + \tau_{xy}^2}$$

$$= \pm\sqrt{\left(\frac{3.5 + 11.3}{2}\right)^2 + 60.5^2}$$

$$= 61.0 \text{ MPa}$$

Note that this is very close to the value for τ_{xy}.

SAQ 2.17

Table 2.9 Comparison of new and failed rivets

	Hardness H_V	Tensile strength/ MPa	Shear strength/ MPa
New rivets	95	385	225
Failed rivets	62	252	160

SAQ 2.18

(a) The shear force acting in the cross section of the panel is:

$$F = \tau A = 60.5 \times 10^6 \ \text{Pa} \times \left(1 \times 10^{-3} \times 50 \times 10^{-3}\right) \text{m}^2 = 3.03 \ \text{kN}$$

(b) The shear stress in a rivet:

$$\tau = \frac{\text{force}}{\text{rivet cross-sectional area}}$$

$$= \frac{3.03 \ \text{kN}}{\frac{\pi}{4}\left(4.75 \times 10^{-3}\right)^2 \ \text{m}^2}$$

$$= 171 \ \text{MPa}$$

SAQ 2.19

In order to achieve a safety factor of 2, the maximum shear stress in the rivet must be half its static strength: $225/2 = 112.5$ MPa.

Assuming the design of the container remains the same, the maximum shear force computed in SAQ 2.18, 3.03 kN, can be used to calculate the required rivet diameter d:

$$d = \sqrt{\frac{3.03 \ \text{kN}}{\frac{\pi}{4} \times 112.5 \times 10^6 \ \text{N m}^{-2}}} = 5.86 \ \text{mm}$$

Specifying a rivet diameter of, say, 6 mm would ensure a safety factor of above 2.

ACKNOWLEDGEMENTS

Grateful acknowledgement is made to the following sources:

FIGURES

Figure 2.1: © Homer Sykes/Corbis.

Figure 2.5: © From http://web4.si.edu/sil/scientific-identity/display_results. cfm?alpha_sort=W

Figure 2.13: © archivberlin Fotoagentur GmbH/Alamy.

Figure 2.12(a): © Sam Ogden/Science Photo Library.

Figure 2.17: From http://en.wikipedia.org/wiki/Image:HOOKE_Robert.jpg

Figure 2.23: © Rolls-Royce.

Figure 2.37: © Alex Bartel/Science Photo Library; © Maximilian Stock Ltd/Science Photo Library.

Figure 2.29: © NASA from http://quest.arc.nasa.gov

COURSE TEAM ACKNOWLEDGEMENTS

This part was prepared for the course team by Martin Rist.

T357 COURSE TEAM

Professor Michael Fitzpatrick (course team chair)

Andy Harding (course manager)

Jackie Burnicle (course manager)

ACADEMIC STAFF

Dr Alun Armstrong	Michael Hush
Professor Adrian Demaid	Dr Peter Lewis
Professor Chris Earl	Dr Jim Moffatt
Professor Lyndon Edwards	Dr Ed Murphy
Dr Salih Gungor	Dr Martin Rist

EXTERNAL ASSESSOR

Professor Lindsay Greer, University of Cambridge

SUPPORT STAFF

Debbie Derbyshire (course team secretary)

Colin Gagg

Stan Hiller

Gordon Imlach

Pete Ledgard

Rehana Malik

PRODUCTION TEAM

Kirsten Barnett	Vicky Eves
Annette Booz	Chris French
Philippa Broadbent	Jonathan Martyn
Lisa Carrick	Katie Meade
Teresa Cox	Lara Mynors
Sarah Crompton	Deana Plummer
Daphne Cross	Lynn Short
Anna Edgley-Smith	